PROJECT DELIVERY SYSTEM

PDS Brings People Together to Achieve Success!

CH2M HILL's Project Delivery System (PDS) is your roadmap to project success and your key to forming stronger ties with customers. This unique approach to planning and executing projects of all sizes works on a simple premise — focus on each project's unique needs and harness the best skills and tools to meet those needs. By applying PDS principles at all phases, project teams improve communication, boost working efficiency, and smooth the journey toward quality results and delighted customers.

CH2MHILL

Project Delivery System

ISBN 0-9652616-0-3
Printed in the United States of America

For further information regarding availability of this book, contact:

CH2MHILL
Project Delivery Coordinator
P.O. Box 22508
Denver, CO 80222-0508
1-866-CH2MPDS (toll free)
(1-866-242-6737)
www.ch2mhill.com/projectdelivery

To our customers

CONTENTS

Preface

CH2M HILL is a global project delivery firm making technology work to help our customers build a better world. We help customers move projects from concept to successful operation. This mission has emerged from changes the firm underwent in the early 1990s to emphasize benchmark performance through the complete delivery of projects. These changes represented a new direction for CH2M HILL, a new direction that required the firm to develop a strategic project management system, which includes a process for consistently delivering high-quality projects to our customers.

Whether they are a business or some other type of organization, many enterprises undergo change. However, few develop a system that fully supports their new direction. Instead, they settle for incremental changes to their project management procedures and skill sets in hopes of improving their ability to manage projects. This approach can provide short-term benefits, but, in the long-term, improving discrete procedures and skills will limit the ability of the enterprise to achieve benchmark performance on project delivery. This system must span all of the new changes an enterprise makes and provide a context for the development and implementation of new procedures and skills. In other words, the system must be the source for and the justification of the incremental changes in the way the enterprise delivers projects to its customers. Without a system that supports and aligns with the strategic direction of the enterprise, it is difficult to determine which changes will improve how the enterprise delivers projects.

CH2M HILL's Project Delivery System (PDS) and the associated project delivery process, which are the topics of this book, represent the firm's commitment to continuous improvement and benchmark performance. CH2M HILL has aggressively installed the system on a global basis, and we strongly believe that its on-going installation will differentiate our firm from others in the industry and will give our customers the high-quality projects and services they demand.

Furthermore, CH2M HILL is sharing this system and philosophy with other enterprises to help them achieve benchmark results as well. It is CH2M HILL's desire that other enterprises benefit from the experience and expertise the firm's project delivery experts offer.

Acknowledgments

CH2M HILL's Project Delivery System (PDS) was developed by CH2M HILL project managers. Teams of project managers worked to provide the firm with a Project Delivery System that has led to unprecedented benchmark performance on the projects we deliver to our customers. This book is one of the outcomes of the work of these teams.

CH2M HILL thanks the project delivery team, whose members developed PDS and oversaw its installation in the firm. Project delivery team members included: Ron Advani, Bill Dehn, John Echternach, Dave Ellison, John Filbert, Dick Foster, John VanDeusen, and Starr Dehn. CH2M HILL also thanks the two process improvement teams that developed the project delivery process, which is the core of PDS and is the focus of this book. The project planning team included: Jeff Mather, Dana Rippon, Mike Dilembo, Ted Way, and Fred Bauhof. The project execution team included: Bud Ahearn, Jim Hawley, Tom Searle, Gene Suhr, and Mike Tilchen. The project execution team members also deserve acknowledgment for authoring early versions of the text for this book.

Project managers have skills for managing projects but do not always have skills for producing books. Fortunately, editors and graphic designers at CH2M HILL do have the skills needed to take ideas about project delivery and clearly describe them in a book. CH2M HILL thanks the following editors, designers, and administrative staff for their contribution to the development and production of this book: Megan Abeyta, Carole Bollmann, Chyrisse Israel, Roy DeLeon, Patty Keck, Gary Means, Kathy Mullen, Judy Panek, Elizabeth Ridley, and Robin Watkins.

Perhaps most important to the success of PDS has been the endorsement and acceptance of the system by our customers. Their positive attitude, encouragement, and constructive feedback have been essential to the teams' abilities to develop, implement, and improve upon PDS. CH2M HILL thanks Mike Kennedy and Ray Topping for their continuing endorsement and support of the PDS Management Consulting Team that provides PDS services to our customers. Consulting team members include Don DeWolfe, Dave Ellison, Gregg Hughes, Craig Lenhart, Juan Salazar, Linda Tiernan, and Jeannine Yancey.

Project Delivery Overview

- The Challenge

- The Solution

- The Project Delivery System (PDS) Defined

- The Benefits

- The PDS Book

The Challenge

A more competitive global marketplace, coupled with an increase in "project-centered" work as the preferred method for delivering value, is fueling renewed interest in achieving greater project realization. Most project-centered enterprises know the equation for project success — consistently produce results that satisfy, but also delight, customers; meet organizational objectives; and fulfill project leader and project team requirements. Yet constant project achievement remains a tremendous challenge for most project-centered enterprises.

The reason for many project disappointments is beguilingly simple. Even in the face of potential consequences as the loss of customers, cost overruns, missed deadlines, and disenchanted project participants, the organizations, project leaders, and project teams may not always follow the known principles of sound project management.

And the consequences can be significant and painful. Recent surveys have estimated that project "fix-up" costs can be 25 percent of an enterprise's operating funds. That 25 percent can be attributed to root causes. In short, projects fail because:

- Planning is inadequate.
- Roles and responsibilities are unclear.
- No process for delivering projects is in place.
- No process for managing change exists.
- Budgeting processes are ineffectual.
- Rewards and recognition are nonexistent.

Figure 1

The Challenge

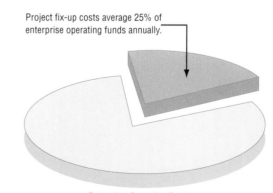

Project fix-up costs average 25% of enterprise operating funds annually.

Enterprise Operating Funds

The Solution

Understanding and applying project leadership principles organized in a system or model such as CH2M HILL's Project Delivery System (PDS) can ensure success. By employing this dynamic system, project-centered enterprises can significantly increase customer satisfaction, organizational effectiveness, financial returns, employee retention, and organizational pride.

We designed the process-driven system around the five fundamental principles of successful project management:

- Focus on customers — and delight them.
- Employ overarching work processes on every project, whether big or small.
- Recognize and reward project leaders and team members — make them an integral part of the project-centered enterprise.
- Put systems in place for performance measurement and continuous learning.
- Define an organizational structure for every project.

Figure 2
PDS comprises four interdependent organizational elements that help people work together to deliver results that delight customers

The Project Delivery System (PDS) Defined

The components of CH2M HILL's PDS are specifically designed to overcome the root causes of project delivery failures and avoid associated fix-up costs:

Customer Relationships

At the heart of PDS is a satisfied and delighted customer. Reaching this level of satisfaction is much more than just achieving technical quality on a project. It's about involving the customer in decisions and offering customer-focused service built around strong relationships.

Overarching Work Processes

Planning and executing project work relies on five overarching work processes (see Figure 3):

Figure 3

- Charter Team — team definition, development and sustainability.
- Plan Project — work definition and scheduling, resource planning, and performance measurement.
- Endorse Project — full endorsement of the workplan by customers, other stakeholders, the project team and the enterprise.
- Manage change — plan and follow, with all parties, a process for managing project change.
- Close Project — identify, budget, and implement closing and learning activities throughout the project.

Project Leadership and Team Sponsorship

Successful project-centered enterprises create a culture that aligns necessary resources with the capability of working interdependently with all project participants.

PDS Tools

Information systems, performance measurements, and learning tools must be in place for success.

Project Enterprise Structure

An organizational structure must be designed for each project to ensure customer focus, leadership commitment, and a collaborative team environment that fosters interdependent participation.

The Benefits

The benefits of CH2M HILL's PDS start with the customers, who receive high-quality projects that routinely meet expectations, costs, and schedule goals. Full recognition and career development is available to project leaders and team members and is connected with performance tools and metrics and learning systems. PDS allows the enterprise to achieve excellence by furnishing a consistent customer focus that is adaptable to the ever-changing demands and challenges of our dynamic business environment.

In short, PDS brings people together to achieve success!

The PDS Book

This PDS Book presents brief topics on customer focus and on project managers as leaders, followed by monographs on each of the five processes introduced above.

Roles and Responsibilities of the Project Manager

OVERVIEW

The title *project manager* is limiting and misleading. Although it emphasizes the importance of overseeing and monitoring a project, it ignores other, more elusive leadership skills that the project manager needs to successfully lead a project to completion. This monograph explores the two roles of a project manager — manager and leader — and the six major responsibilities associated with those roles:

- Focusing on the customer

- Creating the project vision

- Building and maintaining the project team

- Planning the project

- Managing resources

- Ensuring quality

Introduction

> *In management, it is the loss of the big issues, the absence of our concern
> for the important, that has made us slaves to the urgent.*
>
> *David K. Hurst, 1995*

According to Hurst (1995), the issues discussed in this monograph would be "important" rather than "urgent." No one needs to be reminded of urgent issues: they have loud voices, which demand attention and often drown out the important issues. A project manager who is overloaded with urgent issues and who has a packed schedule of activities is probably letting others lead and reacting to others' priorities. However, a project manager who understands his or her roles and associated responsibilities can not only manage the project but can *lead* the project to successful completion.

Project teams have the mission to "improve the economic status and quality of life of all stakeholders" (Covey 1992). In fulfilling this mission, each team member has one or more roles to play; however, the project manager has ultimate responsibility. This monograph describes the roles and associated responsibilities of the project manager.

Two Primary Roles: Leader and Manager

A project manager should incorporate the following responsibilities into management of a project in a way that increases project performance:

- Focusing on the customer

- Creating the project vision

- Building and maintaining the project team

- Planning the project

- Managing resources

- Ensuring quality

During execution of a project, the amount of attention required by each of these responsibilities will vary over time and from one task to another. Some responsibilities will take precedence during periods of rapid change; for example, when starting up the project. Others will only need tending once the project is under way to maintain a steady and proper course. In addition to requiring varying levels of attention, the responsibilities are interdependent; therefore, a weak relationship with the customer can cloud the project vision, making it difficult to identify and meet the customer's expectations.

Because project managers are continually dealing with issues that range from defining vision and strategy to managing technical and administrative details, a project manager must fill two roles, leadership and management. As a leader, the project manager attends to the larger picture: project status in relation to the overall needs and expectations of the customer and the strategic goals of the

*The project manager
leads by considering
the long-range view.*

enterprise. In this role, the project manager is a member of a larger enterprise team, whose members are responsible for preserving and improving the enterprise as a whole. The project manager also leads by considering the long-range view: envisioning the future a project aims to realize, building alignment among stakeholders around the vision, and developing a strategy to achieve the vision.

In addition to serving in the role of leader and looking at the big picture, the project manager is also expected by the enterprise, the customer, and the team to oversee the day-to-day activities of a project and monitor the project's progress. This requires a commitment to using the project delivery process for managing a project, as well as mentoring and coaching other team members toward the same commitment. Management skills provide the basis for overseeing the technical and administrative details of the project and its performance.

To meet these significant and sometimes conflicting roles of manager and leader, the project manager's main asset is the ability to get things done. Since time is a limited resource, project managers must learn to shift smoothly and effectively between the leadership and management roles, which are depicted as two interrelated cycles in Figure 4.

Figure 4. Leadership and Management Cycles

The leadership cycle — envision, align, deploy, learn — comes into play during times when significant transformation is needed; that is, when starting up a project or addressing a major change not covered in the existing workplan. The leadership cycle begins with envisioning the desired response or result and aligning all parties who will be affected by the change with the vision. Strategies needed to implement the change are then deployed, and the cycle is completed as project managers incorporate what they have learned into the next leadership or management cycle.

After deployment, the project manager's role shifts from the leadership cycle to the management cycle. The management cycle — plan, do, check, act — begins with planning for the required activity. Planning is followed by execution of the plans in the form of work processes. As the work is completed, the manager's next task is to check the results to determine if they conform with the expectations defined in the planning step. The final step in the management cycle is to take appropriate action: if activities are proceeding on course, the project manager continues to operate in the management role, repeating the management cycle activities; if significant deviations are encountered, the project manager should respond by taking appropriate corrective action. However, if significant change is required, the project manager must move into the leadership role until a new course of action has been established.

The project manager needs to be capable of operating in both the leadership and management cycles concurrently.

The project manager needs to be capable of operating in both the leadership and management cycles concurrently. For example, the project manager initiates the leadership cycle when a change occurs, to define a solution with the customer; meanwhile, his or her continuing activities in the management cycle ensure that the quality and quantity of work performed by the team does not decline.

Figure 5 frames both the leadership and management roles of a project manager. Although emphasis has traditionally been placed on the management role, this model has an increased emphasis on vision, strategy, and a proactive approach to the management of people, resources, and quality; all activities of a project leader. In this monograph, each of these responsibilities is discussed with an emphasis on the leadership role of the project manager, since this role has traditionally not been acknowledged.

Figure 5. Project Manager Roles of Leadership and Management

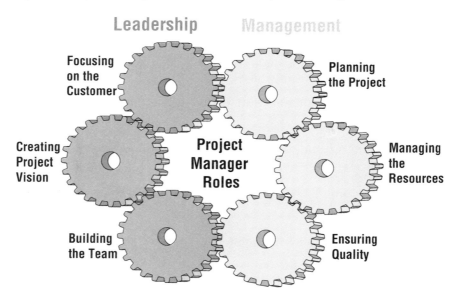

Responsibility 1. Focusing on the Customer

All projects begin and end with the customer. Throughout the life of the project, the project manager is charged with marshaling the forces needed to serve the customer. In this area of responsibility, the project manager is given the full support of the entire management of the enterprise, including the customer service manager or the account manager.

In focusing on the customer, the project manager's duties are to:

- Understand the customer's business needs and expectations, both for the project and for the services.

- Develop the project vision and generate alignment around it.

- Plan for customer involvement, communication, and service.

- Gain endorsement of the project workplan and team charter early and maintain endorsement through meaningful dialogue with the customer during the project.

Methods for Focusing on the Customer

Get to Know the Customer

Implementing a customer focus begins by taking the first opportunity that presents itself to get to know the customer and begin establishing a good relationship. At the outset of a project, this opportunity will likely include discussing the project definition and the customer's vision and expectations and learning about the customer's organization and working environment.

Communicate Continually

Focusing on the customer demands ongoing, personal, two-way communication with as many of the customer's staff members as possible. Listening with sensitivity, rather than talking, is the greater of the two channels of communication. Customers are people, and people want to be acknowledged by having their needs and views heard and understood.

Throughout a project, the entire project team should be actively focused on the customer: keeping the customer up-to-date on the project's progress, building relationships with customer staff, and helping to analyze and define issues and develop alternative courses of action. This will require frequent contact with the customer, most likely at their place of business.

An advantage of having open lines of communication is that a project manager can learn about opportunities for additional services. Customers can and do change their approach and priorities, and these changes can present opportunities for an enterprise to provide additional services.

Cultivate the Relationship

Perhaps the most important method for maintaining a customer focus is to cultivate the customer relationship. Establishing a one-to-one, professional relationship between project managers is a minimal requirement for project success. However, the relationship can go far beyond this and, in the best case, will be the source of trust and good feelings between one organization and another. (See the monograph *Building Customer Relationships*.)

Responsibility 2. Creating the Project Vision

The title of project manager is both limiting and misleading; the people to which this discussion is directed are project *leaders* who can create a vision and inspire people with that vision. This is by far the most important responsibility of the project manager.

> *A well-formed vision has at least seven characteristics. First, it is an end result, not a process. Second, it is a desire, not an obligation. Third, it is specific. To state the obvious, a vision should be capable of being seen. Thus, the vision must be specific enough so you know it when you see it. Fourth, it is not avoiding or ridding yourself of something unwanted. Fifth, it is not limited by what you think is possible. Sixth, it is in present tense. Seventh, it has nothing to do with being number one. Focus on good work, not on standings or recognition.*
>
> *James Saveland, U.S. Forest Service, 1995*

The project vision is the image or understanding of what the project will accomplish and what will be different at the end of the project. Having a project vision is crucial to effective leadership and management of any project. The project vision is the basis for understanding the customer's and the enterprise's expectations for the project and for developing the project definition. Keep in mind that without a project vision, no amount of attention to doing *things right* will get you to the desired state if you are not doing the *right things*.

In creating the vision, the project manager is responsible for the following:

- Envisioning the end of the project and planning a route to its end on the basis of the customer's needs and expectations and the enterprise's business goals.

- Articulating the vision with enthusiasm and charisma; generating buy-in or commitment from all stakeholders; and inspiring people to achieve the vision.

- Modifying the vision and strategy as circumstances change and new opportunities appear. (Although the vision must adapt to the realities of the project as it progresses, the vision must not be continually modified, since it forms the foundation for the customer's needs and expectations and the project's workplan.)

Methods for Creating the Project Vision

Gather Information from Stakeholders

To create a compelling vision, the project manager must first obtain a thorough grasp of the customer's needs and expectations and the business goals of the enterprise. This will require listening carefully to a variety of customer representatives and determining how the enterprise can meet those needs and expectations. The project manager then takes a leadership role in sharing the vision with key stakeholders, inside and outside the enterprise, and in further refining the vision through dialogue.

Meet to Define the Vision

Although the project vision contributes to the project definition in the workplan and the team purpose in the team charter, the various parties can easily draw different interpretations from these documents. Therefore, face-to-face meetings will help clarify expectations and uncover any differences of opinion concerning responsibilities, scope, time, quality, or cost. Holding these meetings at the outset of project planning lowers the potential for misunderstanding and conflict at later stages and builds a shared leadership ethic that can be called upon when issues arise.

The logistics for these meetings will vary with the scale of the project and the organizational cultures and personal styles of the enterprise and people involved. At a minimum, the project manager should schedule an hour or two to meet with his or her counterpart in the customer's organization to discuss their mutual understanding. In larger, more complex projects, the project manager should consider whether there is value to be gained from extending the dialogue and developing a more comprehensive partnering approach.

How will you know when the dialogue is complete? John Kotter offers advice:

> *If you can't communicate the vision to someone in five minutes or less and get a reaction that signifies both understanding and interest, you are not yet done with this phase of the transformation process.*
>
> *John Kotter, 1990*

In meeting to define a vision, four steps are useful to follow:

1. Define what is expected.

2. Identify and resolve the differences.

3. Broaden alignment.

4. Improve continually.

1. Define What Is Expected

Reviewing initial descriptions of the project that have appeared in the request for proposal, the proposal, and the contract is the first step to obtaining a mutual understanding of the project needs, including technical, financial, scheduling, and other objective aspects of the project. The project manager should then give his or her own interpretation of the customer's needs and seek feedback from the customer.

Once the customer representative and project manager have reached a mutual understanding of the project needs, the dialogue should shift to a clarification of the customer's vision for the project: the image or understanding of what the project will accomplish. One way to get the customer representative to articulate their project vision would be to ask him or her to imagine how the finished project might be described in a newspaper article. During this process, refer to the needs you have previously defined and make necessary adjustments in either the objective aspects of the project or the project vision. If, in defining the vision, no differences exist between the customer representative's and project manager's perceptions, this alignment should be expanded to encompass other stakeholders (step 3). If differences do exist, the discussion moves to step 2, where the differences are identified and resolved.

2. Identify and Resolve the Differences

The identification of differences in the project vision should be regarded as a positive event, since it may help to prepare for or eliminate issues that could prevent quality performance at later stages. To have a productive dialogue, the project manager may suggest that differences which emerge during the discussion should be noted, without attempting to resolve them one by one as they develop.

After both parties have had the opportunity to review the entire vision, they can return to the list of differences and strategize on ways to deal with them; for example, sorting them in terms of importance (critical versus noncritical), type (differences in terminology versus differences in concept), or amount of time needed to work through each one. Having sorted through all the differences in vision, they can then decide which differences need to be resolved, when, and by whom. At times, the project manager and the customer representative may find that they will need consultation from additional parties to address certain issues.

In the course of identifying differences in vision, opportunities may surface for creative solutions, which could add value to the project. The project manager should always be aware of this prospect and be prepared to respond.

3. Broaden Alignment

Once the customer and project manager are aligned around the project vision, other key stakeholders must be aligned as the project moves forward.

Once the customer and project manager have resolved the differences and are aligned around the project vision, other key stakeholders must be aligned as the project moves forward. Communicating the vision to other stakeholders also tests whether the dialogue is complete. As a third stage in their own dialogue on vision, the project manager and customer representative may want to strategize the best means for broadening the alignment.

An optimal strategy for broadening alignment will vary with the scale and complexity of the project as well as the preferred styles and capabilities of the project manager and customer representative. On the one hand, they may prefer to separately communicate results to their own organizations, including project team members. On the other hand, they may see value in bringing all parties together to work collaboratively on articulating the vision, identifying potential obstacles, building commitment, and shaping strategies.

Once the vision has been articulated, it must be communicated in a manner that helps stakeholders understand and buy into it. This activity often occurs as an initial part of the project team's chartering process and includes opportunities for team members to contribute to refining the vision. (See the monograph *Charter Team*.)

4. Improve Continually

To bring the dialogue to closure, the project manager must commit to revisiting the vision during the course of project planning and execution. Once the project has begun, the weight of everyday events will likely drive the project manager's attention to the urgent issues. Making a commitment to revisit the vision will ensure that you do not lose sight of the longer-term details. As you meet over the course of the project, always include revisiting the vision as an agenda item. If the project and vision drift apart, the project manager should be alert for possible problems with scope, schedule, or quality, and investigate further.

Responsibility 3. Building and Maintaining the Project Team

A strong team, which takes time and care to develop, is vital to the success of any project. The project manager is responsible for selecting the right people for the team and for helping them to become an effective working unit. The project manager must develop a high level of comfort in working with groups, a basic familiarity with the stages of group development, and a good grasp of basic group facilitation skills.

Some aspects of team development that may at first appear dysfunctional are actually appropriate for the early stages of group development. For example, before team members know each other well enough to begin voicing their opinions and perspectives, they will test the purposes and roles of other team members. This team behavior might be manifested in the form of questions or disagreements concerning specific duties or quibbling about specific definitions or techniques. The effective team leader will understand what the team is going through and respond appropriately by maintaining a focus on the larger goals, eliciting a range of perspectives and opinions, and achieving closure on critical issues.

Finding and keeping good team members, informing them, and clearly defining responsibilities are more important than direct day-to-day oversight of individual work.

Leadership of the project team involves preserving, protecting, and improving the productive capability of people — the most valuable resource available to the project manager. In addition, the project manager is charged with directing day-to-day work and selecting short-term priorities. However, finding and keeping good team members, informing them, and clearly defining responsibilities are more important than direct day-to-day oversight of individual tasks. If the project delivery process is followed, short-term changes in direction and continuous oversight should not be required.

Methods for Building and Maintaining the Project Team

Find Good People

The project manager must identify the most appropriate people to fill available positions on the team. It is like the National Football League free-agent draft: design the team and fill key spots. A personal network and considerable knowledge of the capabilities of the enterprise's people are very helpful in designing a top-notch team. New project managers need the dedicated support of the enterprise's management in order to assemble and maintain a quality team.

One key to success in team leadership is to assemble the most skilled people and retain them in spite of the lure from competing projects. The project manager must constantly reinforce his or her commitment to the team and work to preserve the integrity of the team. Eternal vigilance is required.

Keep Good People

In order to keep good people on the job, the project manager should fully empower the team to meet the project expectations. To meet these expectations, members must have a good sense of individual and collective responsibilities. There should also be clear, mutual understanding of project expectations in five areas: desired results, guidelines for obtaining the results, resources available to get the job done, accountability for deliverables, and positive versus negative consequences associated with performance (Covey 1992). If the team understands these expectations and responsibilities, then they will be motivated and empowered to meet them. These expectations can be most effectively communicated within the context of a team chartering session, at the outset of a project.

Inform Team Members

A general understanding of what the whole team is doing can be of immense importance for individual effectiveness and morale. Therefore, the project manager must keep team members from working in isolation by providing general news and reporting progress to the team. The "need to know" is an intrinsic desire of team members.

Attend to Individual Needs

Improving team capability also requires attending to the professional development of individual team members. The project schedule must allow time for individual attention and professional improvement through coaching and counseling. All team members must know that they are valued and that their progress is important to the project manager as well as to the enterprise.

Clearly Define Assignments and Responsibilities

Assuming the team is well informed and attended to and morale is high, then the project manager must give clear direction concerning assignments and responsibilities. Even if the team understands the project expectations, team members must know how to accomplish the assignment and have the personal confidence to ask for help when they need it.

Reward and Recognize

Lastly, as achievements occur, the project manager needs to make sure the team members receive proper reward and recognition. Everyone who has contributed to achieving the vision should be congratulated in some way to validate their contribution to the project's success.

Responsibility 4. Planning the Project

Once the vision has been defined and agreed upon and the team has been formed, the focus must shift to planning the project, in particular to the elaboration of concrete strategies for achieving the goals of the project. The duties of the project manager in planning the project include:

- Developing a workplan in which the customer's vision and the enterprise's definition of the project coincide. (See the monograph *Plan Project*.)

- Involving the team members, customer, and others in further articulation and endorsement of the workplan.

- Ensuring that all components that support project delivery, including processes, people, tools, and skills, remain aligned with the vision, in balance with each other, and well integrated during execution of the workplan.

- Creating opportunities to add value throughout the project.

Methods for Planning the Project

Set Aside Time

Time should be set aside for strategic planning and developing the project definition with key members of the project team.

Enlist Help

Experienced or intuitive people from outside the day-to-day team, even with something less than full knowledge of the project's details, can often help analyze opportunity quickly and effectively.

Foster Participation

The creativity and productivity of strategy sessions can be increased by fostering open participation in a casual, relaxed atmosphere, as free as possible from fear of negative judgment or hierarchical dominance. Too many perceived constraints or negative assumptions can kill the creativity needed for effective planning. In fact, the only legitimate constraint at this stage is that the team serves in the best interest of the customer.

Brainstorm

Avoid selecting solutions or taking immediate action until ideas are thoroughly worked through and a full grasp of the project has been developed, including interrelationships among the various project elements. Since project managers cannot control everything that will happen once projects start, they should prioritize their efforts and invest in those areas that have the greatest potential for achieving the desired results.

Plan from the End to the Beginning

Strategy development can be facilitated by planning from the project's completion backward to the present. This process is easier if the vision and expectations are mutually agreed upon and well defined.

Plan for Change

Change is inevitable in any human undertaking and must be planned for. Change can be an opportunity to add value by reducing cost or enhancing performance. However, in order to have this perspective, the project manager must be able to identify the potential benefits associated with change, must be willing to take risks, and must be capable of recruiting others to share in those risks. (See the monograph *Manage Change*.)

Responsibility 5. Managing Resources

Once a project has been launched, managing its resources — especially the resources of time and money — becomes a major focus of the project manager's work.

The primary reason to keep records of time and money is to provide a clear grasp of where the project is, compared to where the project should be at any moment. Whether the project proceeds as planned or encounters change, the project manager must use resources wisely to satisfy the customer and to make a meaningful contribution to the viability of the enterprise.

Once a project has been launched, managing its resources becomes a major focus of the project manager.

Another reason to keep financial records and schedules is that customers occasionally ask for assistance in planning their project and budgeting their work. In order to respond, the enterprise must have developed and monitored its own schedules and budgets.

Keep in mind that focusing on computer spreadsheets does not eliminate the need to attend to the other responsibilities of project management, particularly responsibilities that have a large leadership component. Some project managers get caught up in tracking the project, while other activities that can have a greater effect on project success are ignored.

The project manager's duties with regard to project resources are to:

- Plan adequate resources to ensure health, safety, and environmental protection goals are met.

- Assess technology and resource requirements.

- Obtain the most skilled resources possible and use the right skills, knowledge, and tools at the right time.

- Prepare accurate, realistic budgets, endorsed by the team and customer.

- Include sufficient amounts in the budget to cover the most likely contingencies.

- Plan the cash flow.

- Prepare a reasonable, flexible schedule that achieves the customer's needs without crisis deadlines and unreasonable overtime.

- Prepare accurate assessments of progress in relation to budget and schedule.

- Maintain adequate project records.

- Keep project costs within the customer's available funds so that there are no surprises.

- Aim to complete the essential work with time and money left over.

Methods for Managing the Resources

Use Appropriate Management Tools

The principal tool to be used in project control as well as planning is software for budgeting and scheduling. CH2M HILL has its own management information software, which can be supplemented with other software, such as Microsoft Excel, for analysis and reporting and Primavera or Microsoft Project for schedule development and reporting.

Develop Appropriate Reporting Formats

Progress reporting formats that meet the needs of the customer, the project team, and the enterprise's financial managers must be developed. Reporting formats are one area where the project can either fall short of expectations or add value for the customer. To add value, the project manager must identify what information is wanted, in what format, and at what intervals. If any data are not readily available in the desired form, the project manager will need to weigh the additional costs associated with specialized reports versus the advantages of standard reports.

Monitor Resources

Project managers should minimize the effort required to monitor the use of the accounting system, while still preventing unwanted budget and schedule problems.

Enlist Help

A project assistant, if available, can take responsibility for keeping the project data and records current.

Responsibility 6. Ensuring Quality

Ensuring quality is a leadership responsibility of the project manager. This responsibility cannot be delegated; however, expertise and experience can be found throughout the enterprise to help fulfill this responsibility.

Quality is variously defined as meeting customer expectations, meeting industry standards, and meeting agreed-upon project requirements. The project leader must establish which definitions are appropriate to a specific project and incorporate these standards into a quality management plan, which is an integral part of the project workplan. (See the monograph *Developing the Workplan*.)

One old-fashioned element of quality that every customer expects is attention to detail in all that we do.

One old-fashioned element of quality that every customer expects is attention to detail in all parts of the project. Creating precise plans and managing the plans to ensure attention to detail is fundamental to ensuring quality control. In planning the project, the project manager should put in place processes that make quality a continuous element throughout delivery of the project. For example, senior staff can be recruited to critique and improve on the proposed quality plan for the project. Although the project manager need not personally review every detail of the project, in order to achieve high quality, he or she must commit time to assess quality issues with a team that has collective expertise in all of the project's technologies and practices. Quality control must be well integrated into the project workplan and must be able to accommodate change.

Methods for Ensuring Quality

Select Quality-Oriented Team Members

Aim to get the best people for each assignment; provide training in quality, if needed. Insist on attention to detail, such as checking for technical accuracy, editing text and graphics, and preparing presentable draft products. Make each person responsible for his or her own work, and encourage them to seek out and use experts in areas where they are not fully competent. Articulate quality standards; design quality into projects from the start.

Set an Example

The project manager is personally accountable for quality and the quality management plan.

The project manager is personally accountable for quality and the quality management plan. At the outset of a project, the project manager can begin setting the standards for quality through a combination of thoughtful explanation of the requirements and personal examples. By clarifying expectations, the project manager will help ensure that processes, procedures, and tools for ensuring quality will be adopted and implemented. By modeling desired behaviors — promulgating pride without arrogance, providing a quality work atmosphere, and instilling a calm, orderly work process without panic deadlines or long hours — the project manager will increase the likelihood of these systems being effectively implemented.

Develop a Quality Management Plan

The quality management plan, which is part of the project workplan, outlines the quality processes that should be followed throughout the project. The quality criteria of the customer, the enterprise, and the team need to be incorporated into the quality management plan. In addition, most projects will need to include the quality criteria of additional third-party stakeholders, such as regulators.

In all instances, the criteria included in the plan should be framed in concrete, measurable terms: time, cost, product specifications, and performance levels.

Gain Team Buy-In of the Plan

The quality management plan is then communicated to the team, with the understanding that it must be realized, whatever contingencies might arise. Realigning the plan will require careful, timely monitoring and corrective action on the part of designated team members, and it may entail training team members who are unfamiliar with quality control and assurance procedures. Input should also be encouraged from team members on methods to improve quality of service. Insist on and encourage the learning of new and improved methods and techniques.

Input should also be encouraged from team members on methods to improve quality of service.

Project Manager Skills for Career Development

In order to effectively perform the six leadership and management responsibilities described in this monograph, the project manager will need to achieve a basic level of competency in five interrelated skill sets, including business, interpersonal, project management, practice and technology, and customer service.

Business Skills

Business skills enable proper management of the project's resources. These skills provide the project manager with an ability to anticipate when and how personnel, materials, and funds will need to flow into and through the project; to monitor and adjust actual flow of those resources; to determine levels of profitability for the enterprise; and to ensure budget and cash flow meet both customer and enterprise requirements.

Interpersonal Skills

Because a project manager's work demands coordination and integration of activities on the part of many individuals, interpersonal skills are essential for effective project management. Excellence in this area begins with an awareness of several facets of personal style and their effect on interpersonal relations in the project context.

Equally important are preferred approaches to supervising team members, making decisions, solving problems, and handling conflict. In this regard, Stephen Covey's concept of principle-centered leadership is important (Covey 1992). Covey advocates that principles be instilled, along with practices, as a means of fully empowering team members to do their jobs.

Interpersonal skills also encompass a range of communication practices, including effective listening; sharing of one's own thoughts, feelings, values, information, and ideas; and giving and receiving feedback.

Project Management Skills

Project management skills include techniques needed to manage project scope, schedule, and work processes. The basic requirements include mastery of tools and procedures for work planning, project execution, and closeout. The project manager can increase chances for success by improving strengths in personal organization, delegation, time management, and change management.

Practice and Technology Skills

For smaller projects, the project manager may also be the lead engineer. For large projects, the project manager will more likely oversee multiple personnel, some of whom will have greater technical expertise in certain areas than the project manager. In either case, the final responsibility for seeing that appropriate technology is selected and applied on the project and that the results are well aligned with the customer's expectations rests with the project manager.

Customer Service Skills

The development of customer service precedes the startup of the project, encompasses project execution, and continues long after project completion. The project manager must understand the value of customer service and the skills through which a healthy relationship can be built.

Summary

A capable project manager routinely and appropriately divides his or her time between the leadership and management roles and the six responsibilities that have been described in this monograph and are summarized in Table 1 (see next page). This effort must be proactive and planned; it will not happen automatically. Planning must be accompanied by the self-discipline to follow the plan. Delegating work or sharing portions of these responsibilities is a reasonable and necessary practice; however, the ultimate responsibilities cannot be delegated, nor can fault for failure be passed on to the project team. Although the work within these responsibilities is of long-term rather than short-term importance, regular attention is needed to ensure that the methods described in this monograph are used to fulfill each responsibility.

Table 1. Summary of Project Manager's Roles and Responsibilities

Leadership Role					
CUSTOMER	**VISION**	**TEAM**	**PLANNING**	**RESOURCES**	**QUALITY**
• Obtain alignment with the vision and expectations. • Gain endorsement of the plan.	• Articulate the project vision. • Grasp the bigger picture. • Take a long-term view.	• Recruit the best mix of talent for the job. • Align the team with the vision. • Inspire the team. • Synergize efforts. • Develop the team. • Mentor team members. • Recognize results and reward the team.	• Create an optimal plan. • Create opportunities to add value. • Manage risks.	• Obtain the best resources.	• Articulate quality standards. • Be personally accountable. • Continually improve.

Management Role					
CUSTOMER	**VISION**	**TEAM**	**PLANNING**	**RESOURCES**	**QUALITY**

• Develop and manage a client service plan.
• Develop strong communication strategies.
	• Monitor compliance with vision (manage scope).	• Assess staffing requirements.
		• Assess team skills.
		• Collaborate.
		• Delegate.
		• Manage the team.
		• Supervise and coach.
			• Execute the plan.
			• Manage change.
				• Assess resource requirements.
				• Manage and preserve resources.
				• Maintain a project records system.
					• Manage quality standards:
					  – Monitor
					  – Measure
					  – Control

References

Covey, Stephen. 1992. *Principle-Centered Leadership.* New York: Simon & Schuster.

Hurst, David K. 1995. *Crisis and Renewal: Meeting the Challenge of Organizational Change.* Cambridge, MA: Harvard Business School Press.

Kotter, John. 1990. *A Force for Change: How Leadership Differs from Management*. New York: Free Press.

Saveland, James. 1995. "Fire in the Forest." Paper presented at National Silviculture Workshop, May 8-11. Mescalero, New Mexico. RM-GTR-267.

Other Resources

Block, Peter. 1987. *The Empowered Manager: Positive Political Skills at Work*. San Francisco: Jossey-Bass.

Hitt, William. 1988. *The Leader-Manager: Guidelines for Action*. Columbus, OH: Battelle Press.

Koestenbaum, Peter. 1991. *Leadership: The Inner Side of Greatness*. San Francisco: Jossey-Bass.

Senge, Peter. 1991. *The Fifth Discipline: The Art and Practice of the Learning Organization*. New York: Doubleday.

Shainis, Murray; Anton Dekom; and Charles McVinney. 1995. *Engineering Management: People and Projects*. Columbus, OH: Battelle Press.

Vaill, Peter. 1989. *Managing as a Performing Art: New Ideas for a World of Chaotic Change*. San Francisco: Jossey-Bass.

Weisbord, Marvin. 1987. *Productive Workplaces: Organizing and Managing for Dignity, Meaning, and Community*. San Francisco: Jossey-Bass.

Build Customer Relationships

OVERVIEW

At the core of the Project Delivery System (PDS) is a satisfied customer. And in today's market, customer satisfaction is based on more than just the technical quality of a project. To remain competitive, the enterprise must offer excellent, customer-focused service. The foundation of this service is the strong relationship that develops between people and, ultimately, between organizations.

This monograph focuses on the knowledge and skills that project managers need to develop a strong customer relationship, including:

- The structures and types of customer relationships

- The need to understand a customer's vision, needs, and expectations

- The role that customer service plays in the relationship, and guidelines for customer service

- The need for an explicit communication system

- Guidelines for conflict resolution

Introduction

Technology-based project delivery enterprises, like all service companies, depend on customers. We serve the needs of our customers and, in doing so, have built a business that enables us to pursue work that we find satisfying. Our interest in technology does not drive us to design a bridge; the customer's need for that bridge and their willingness to pay for our expertise ensures our continued success. Although the products and services offered may change, our customers remain a constant and central focus. This is why the customer must always be paramount in the project manager's mind and customer satisfaction is the hub of the project delivery process.

Surveys show that customers believe that the service provided is as much as 50 percent of the value they receive.

Customer satisfaction is the most important value-added differentiator. Surveys show that customers believe that the service provided is as much as 50 percent of the value they receive. Technical skills are available from a wide variety of sources, so customers are increasingly using service as the differentiator that determines which enterprise they hire.

Customer satisfaction requires building and maintaining a strong relationship with the customer. Almost always, the correlation between customer relationships and customer satisfaction is perfect: the stronger the customer relationship, the more satisfied the customer. Also, strong relationships make the project manager's job easier and more pleasant, make the customer much more comfortable with the enterprise, and make the enterprise more likely to receive repeat business.

In CH2M HILL's four-stage procurement and performance process, the project manager begins developing customer relationships in the first stage, *planning*. Development of the relationship continues through the *positioning* and *persuasion* phases and then through the fourth and final stage, *performance*, when the customer relationship becomes one of six major responsibilities of the project manager. (See the monograph *Roles and Responsibilities of the Project Manager*.) When combined with the quality of the service provided and the project delivered during the performance phase, the customer relationship becomes the basis for positioning efforts for the next project. That project may be with the same customer, with a customer who has been referred by a satisfied customer, or with a customer who recognizes the enterprise as having an excellent reputation.

The success of the customer relationship during the project depends on numerous factors. This monograph describes five factors that are highly significant to successful customer relationships:

- Structures and types of relationships

- Customer understanding

- Customer service

- Communications

- Conflict resolution and change management

Structures and Types of Relationships

Defining the Structure of Relationships

The success of customer relations is largely based on the structure of the relationship between the project manager and the customer. Although the entire team must try to have an open, respectful, and supportive relationship with the customer, the project manager is the one who can establish and maintain a partnership between the customer and team. Establishing and maintaining the customer relationship is a leadership role of the project manager. (See the monograph *Roles and Responsibilities of the Project Manager*.)

The relationship between the project manager and the customer's project manager is built on trust and mutual commitment.

The relationship between the project manager and the customer's project manager must be one where two leaders are acting interdependently. It is a dynamic relationship where each may, at different times, play the prime leadership role. Fundamentally, the relationship is based on trust and a mutual commitment to providing the services and products that meet the customer's needs and expectations.

The relationship between the enterprise's project manager and the customer's project manager is not the result of good luck, making the customer feel good, or either party's great personality. Its success is based on both parties' understanding and agreeing to the relationship's structure. The structure may be developed formally, through a contractual agreement like partnering, or informally, through discussions between the project manager and the customer. However, when the agreement is reached, each party must act with integrity, strive for open communications, and treat the other party with respect and common courtesy.

In establishing a structure for the relationship, the project manager should consider others in the enterprise who also have responsibilities for customer relationships. Certain individuals who have long-standing relationships with selected customers need to be designated to act as the enterprise's representatives. These people should be responsible for specific customer relationships over the long-term: before projects are identified, while projects are executed, and after projects are completed.

The enterprise's project manager needs to start building his or her own relationships with the customer as early as possible as a foundation for the entire project. The project manager's efforts to build the relationship are made easier if the enterprise's customer service manager has been maintaining ongoing relationships with the customer. The project manager can then leverage the relationship created by the customer service manager, taking care not to disturb the existing relationship the customer service manager has created with the customer. This will require careful planning with the customer service manager.

The customer service manager has the responsibility for developing more than one relationship within the customer's organization, so that if the customer's staff changes, strong relationships with the customer still exist. The relationships developed by the customer service manager become increasingly important as the project winds down and the staff and project manager are reassigned. In this way, continuity is maintained between projects.

Understanding Types of Relationships

In discussing relationships, the following four types of relationships are helpful in describing the different levels of understanding and trust that develop between individuals and between organizations:

- Casual relationship

- Professional relationship

- Personal relationship

- Organizational relationship

At a minimum, the project manager must establish a professional relationship to work collaboratively with the customer.

The initial goal of relationship building by the project manager should be to establish the casual relationship and then develop it to the level of a professional relationship as quickly as possible. At a minimum, the project manager must establish a professional relationship to work collaboratively with the customer throughout the project. Although a personal relationship can strengthen a professional one, the ultimate goal of the enterprise is to move the relationship to the organizational level, which is described later in this section.

With a new customer, the initiation of a casual relationship is usually the starting point. Here we find common ground that lets the project manager get acquainted and become involved with the customer. This involvement includes beginning to understand the customer's style, needs, and interests. With this understanding, the project manager can begin to structure the relationship.

Moving the relationship to the professional level is a necessity. The professional relationship is the level at which both parties have mutual respect for the capabilities of one another and have established working procedures that emphasize their individual strengths. On occasion, each can help further the professional career of the other. For example, the enterprise's project manager could help the customer's project manager achieve recognition within a particular professional society.

Projects generally have problems if the project managers have not developed a professional relationship. Failure to achieve a professional relationship is a signal that the customer is unsure of a project manager's or the enterprise's professionalism. In this situation, the customer will start double-checking the enterprise's work, because the customer will not have confidence in the enterprise's or the project manager's ability to deliver the services contracted. Developing a professional relationship early in the project is clearly the key to success during planning, execution, and closeout.

Developing strong personal relationships between the enterprise's project manager and the customer's project manager is highly desirable and should be attempted. This will require a great deal of commitment and a high level of trust between the two leaders. Some customer representatives may not want a personal relationship but, rather, prefer to keep the relationship on a professional level. In this case, the project manager may be able to develop a personal relationship with one or more people within the customer's organization and build on this. Although a good personal relationship between the project manager and customer representatives enhances the professional relationship, it is not essential. The lack of a personal relationship between the project manager and customer is not an excuse for a poor professional relationship.

The organizational relationship is the level at which the enterprise, the project, and the customer can benefit most. At this level, the enterprise has as much credibility with the customer as does a person who has a strong professional and personal relationship with a member of the customer's staff. The organizational relationship usually requires good relationships both vertically and horizontally within the customer's organization and requires the efforts of many members of the enterprise. If we can achieve a strong organizational relationship within the life of the project, then the project will benefit. If we can do it over a long period of time with the customer on several projects, then the enterprise will benefit through repeat business; the customers will benefit through the expanded knowledge of the capabilities the enterprise can bring to their projects; and new project managers will benefit because customers tend to feel more comfortable with individuals when they feel comfortable with the enterprise. Because everyone benefits in this type of relationship, the organizational relationship should be the ultimate goal for developing relationships with customers.

Customer Understanding

Behavior Patterns and Styles

Relationship building takes time, particularly time spent with the customer representative. Using your observation of the customer representative's social style and behavior can speed up the process of moving beyond the casual relationship to the professional relationship. The key is observation of the customer representatives and identification of their social styles: amiable, analytical, driver, or expressive. (See Social Styles on the next page.) As you listen and watch them closely, what do they react to? Once you have a grasp of social styles, adjust your approach to match them. For example, people with different social styles prefer to receive information in different ways. Analytical types like a list of data and are usually thoughtful and reflective; providing conceptual information by phone will irritate more than inform. However, if a customer representative has an expressive social style, this form of communication would be fine. Therefore, make choices that match the person's style.

Social Styles

A person's social style is the way he or she deals most efficiently and comfortably with all the situations encountered in the course of a day. Following are typical characteristics of four common social styles and the types of responses that are most appropriate.

Analytical
- Systematic thinker and analyst
- Task-oriented
- Reluctant to make decisions without full data

Response: Be thorough; use logic

Driver
- Independent and action-oriented
- Efficient and to the point
- Impatient with delays

Response: Be concise; point out alternatives

Amiable
- Personal relationship- and support-oriented
- Trusting
- Concerned with feelings of others
- Risk averse

Response: Provide reassurance; be ready to compromise

Expressive
- Intuitive and inspirational
- Enthusiastic
- Likely to act on opinions, hunches, and intuition

Response: Respond quickly; be creative

People habitually use their own social styles in their interactions because that is the most efficient and comfortable way for them to achieve their goals and meet their needs. In building relationships, however, project managers should accept that they are obligated to adjust their style to the customer representative's, not vice versa. Project managers will find that their efforts to match their delivery to the customer representative's style will pay dividends. Understanding the social styles of the customer will lead to stronger customer relationships and a clearer understanding of the customer's expectations.

Vision and Expectations

Once the structure of the relationship between the project manager and the customer is established, the project manager must work to manage that relationship by increasing his or her knowledge of the customer. The goal of getting to know the customer is to understand the customer's needs and expectations (see next page) and strengths and weaknesses. Gaining this understanding and then placing it in the proper context of the customer's vision for the project will provide a path for effectively leading the project. The vision is the driving force behind the project, and a good relationship with the customer requires a clear understanding of this vision.

The project vision is the image or understanding of what the project will accomplish. Although a basic description of the expected results should be available in writing, the various parties can easily draw different interpretations from the documentation. Therefore, discussions will help clarify the vision and the associated expectations and identify any differences in interpretation. At the end of these discussions, the project manager must be able to answer "yes" to the following four questions:

1. Does the customer have a clear vision of the successful outcome of the project?

2. Are the workplan and charter aligned with the vision?

3. Are the customer's expectations aligned with that vision?

4. Do the vision and expectations of the project manager and the project team match the customer's?

Every component of the project delivery process will be affected by the degree to which the project manager can confidently answer "yes" to each of these questions.

Needs and Expectations

Differentiating between needs and expectations is important. Needs are the objective, concrete aspects of a project, including technical, financial, and schedule. For example, a customer *needs* a bridge by a certain date for a certain amount of money. However, the customer's expectations will go beyond the needs of the project to encompass more subjective elements. For example, a customer's expectations of a bridge might include aesthetics of the design, public acceptance of the project, or that it be an award-winning bridge. Some of the customer's expectations may not be in the bid request, but they are in the thoughts of the customer representative. Therefore, a bridge that is functionally perfect but not architecturally stimulating may meet the needs of the customer but not meet their expectations, resulting in their dissatisfaction. The project manager must continually monitor the customer's needs and expectations to ensure they are met.

The process for guiding and assisting the customer in clarifying the vision and setting expectations depends on the skills of the project manager (see the monograph *Roles and Responsibilities of the Project Manager*) and the project manager's relationship with the customer's project manager. Clearly, to be successful, the project manager's relationship with the customer must be at least at the professional level.

The following are examples of items to consider when working with the customer to set or manage expectations:

- Identify expectations implied or stated in the contract and proposal.

- Match expectations to scope, schedule, and budget.

- Review expectations with stakeholders both inside and outside of the customer's organization.

- Identify major outcomes of the project and how those outcomes relate to the stakeholders.

- Consider customer expectations of product and service, especially regarding their views on quality.

- Resolve outstanding issues associated with expectations so that there are no unreconciled expectations.

Strengths and Limitations

As important as understanding a customer's vision and expectations is knowing a customer's strengths and limitations. The project manager is responsible for recognizing the customer's strengths, for capitalizing on the value they can bring to the project, and for recognizing the customer's limitations and compensating for them so that they are not detrimental to the project.

Learning about the customer's strengths and limitations requires the ability to ask questions in a nonthreatening way, listen with the goal of understanding, and have empathy for the customer. These skills are helpful in discerning the customer's priorities, infrastructure, funding, preferred contracting strategies, and approaches to risk and change management.

The learning process is not limited to the project manager learning about the customer. Through all of the project manager's interactions with the customer, the customer is learning about him or her. It is essential that the customer learn about the project manager, the team's competencies, and the value that the enterprise brings to the project. Each interaction between the project manager and the customer must move the relationship closer to the organizational level, where the most benefits can be found for all parties.

Customer Service

Customer service is the ability to translate your understanding of customer needs and expectations into specific deliverables that add value for a customer.

Customer service is the ability to translate your understanding of customer needs and expectations into specific deliverables that add value for a customer as the project progresses to completion. Relationships are the conduit for customer service. In turn, customer service reinforces and strengthens relationships. Because customer service is as real as technical products, it can be defined, planned, managed, and evaluated using tools similar to those we use to define, plan, manage, and evaluate technical products.

Customer Service Plan

The process of developing a project workplan guides the customer and the project manager as they work together to establish a common vision, expectations, and goals for the project as a whole. (See the monograph *Plan Project.*) One component of the project workplan, the customer service plan, can help the project manager and the customer agree on what service the customer values and how the enterprise will provide that service.

A customer service plan will provide direction for the project team and ensure common service goals are met. The customer representative and the project manager work together to understand the services the customer wants and develop a plan for providing that service. The project team must then endorse that plan, committing to work together to achieve it.

The customer service plan can be translated into specific deliverables, called service products. Service products are not always tangible deliverables, but they can be defined and documented like any other deliverable. Some specific service products that customers find valuable include: receiving regular status reports that document the information they have requested, regular invoices that compare charges with the predictions of the budget and schedule, meeting minutes within 24 hours of a meeting, and calls returned within a certain amount of time. Once the service products have been defined, the project manager is responsible for ensuring that the project team meets the obligations.

While the project manager and customer representative develop the customer service plan, they will discuss routine interactions that may identify other service products of importance to the customer. Some routine interactions to discuss include:

- Preproposal issues
- The selection process
- Contract negotiations
- Project kickoff and other meetings
- Coordination
- Project status communications
- Project follow-up
- Billing

Asking the customer representative to talk about his or her best customer service experience can also help the project manager understand the service the customer values and can generate more ideas for service products.

Customer Service Guidelines

In addition to developing a customer service plan with service products, our relationships with our customers can be greatly enhanced by incorporating the following six guidelines of customer service into our day-to-day operations:

1. **Accessibility.** Customers want project managers and team members to be available to them at all times. The challenge is to make it seem as though the customer has easy, instant access to project team members.

2. **Attention.** No matter how large or small the project, every customer representative expects his or her job to be at the top of the project manager's list. Knowing this, the project manager must develop consistent practices that reinforce the customer's view. For example, never tell the customer representative that another job is interfering with his or her project.

3. **Follow-through.** Following through on commitments develops the customer's trust in the enterprise. Follow-through applies not just to the technical aspects of the project but also to follow-through on other commitments that shape the customer's view, for example, meeting deadlines for deliverables.

4. **No Surprises.** Never surprise the customer. Project managers should set up the project so that potential problems will be identified early and either averted or discussed with the customer before they become real problems.

5. **Recovery.** Service recovery is the timely correction of service problems to the customer's satisfaction. Relationships remain strong when the customer is confident that the project manager will do what it takes to correct a problem.

6. **Responsiveness.** Responsiveness demonstrates to customers the willingness to adapt to meet their needs and expectations. It does not mean that the project manager will do anything the customer asks or will compromise professional requirements. But, effective project managers seek to manage projects so that they best suit the customer.

Each of these guidelines provides an opportunity to strengthen customer relationships by demonstrating competence, an understanding of the customer's expectations, and a commitment to meeting those expectations.

A Communication System

The success of customer relationships can be enhanced if an explicit system is established for maintaining communication between the project manager and the customer. Because much of the information needed to establish such a system will emerge only during discussions with the customer and other stakeholders, project managers will, in effect, be building this road as they walk it. For this reason, it is essential to include a plan-do-check-act cycle into the communication system.

In the absence of a system for consistent communication, we tend to communicate with the customer by exception.

The need for such a system is clear. In the absence of a system for consistent communication, we tend to communicate with the customer by exception — as the need arises. Unfortunately, most of these circumstances are negative or at least problematic. Therefore, over time the perception develops that a phone call from the customer or project manager typically signals a problem or difficulty. This sets the stage for a negative relationship, although this was certainly not the original intent of either the project manager or the customer representative.

The solution is a proactive system that is designed to ensure communication on a regular basis. The questions to be asked in designing such a system include the following:

- What are the contractual elements of the communication system?

- How often does the customer want regular communication and interaction?

- What is the customer's preferred communication style? For what types of information?

- What are the major topics that should be included in your communication system?

- Who should be included in the communication loop and for what types of communications?

When these questions have been addressed, you should have the basic information needed to develop a communication system. The questions can be viewed as part of the check portion of the ongoing plan-do-check-act cycle. If the project manager has trouble answering any of these questions, he or she probably needs to adjust some part of the communication plan. If the quality of customer relationship is less than ideal, the answers can be used as diagnostics of what is wrong and begin to develop an appropriate response.

Once the customer communication system has been put into practice, the project manager's responsibility is to ensure that the system is clearly understood and used. This will require that a monitoring method be established as part of the overall system. One method is to develop a series of questions that can serve as a metric for the effectiveness of the communication system. For example, if the customer relationship is functioning optimally, the project manager should be able to give a positive answer to each of the following questions:

In the enterprise's relationship with this customer on this project, do we have:

- Open and honest communication, including listening?

- Mutual respect and trust?

- A shared vision of the future for the project?

- Complementary expectations that lead to that vision?

- Clarity of objectives?

- Well-defined roles, responsibilities, and accountability?

- Shared gains or benefits as well as risks?

- Continuity of principal contacts?

- Commitment to continuous improvement of the relationship?

- A conflict — or problem — resolution process?

If the quality of customer relations is less than ideal, the project manager should be able to use the communication system to identify where the difficulty is and begin to develop an appropriate response. One likely place to begin improving relations is to obtain feedback from the customer representative about what he or she has liked best or valued most about this project over the past few months; what he or she has not liked or has valued least; what suggestions he or she has for improvement; and what potential issues or opportunities might affect the project in the future.

Building successful customer relationships takes time and hard work. This is especially true if there is a clash of styles, a misunderstanding, or a shortage of resources for communication. To overcome such barriers, the project manager must be able to tap effective communication skills and develop procedures for preserving the relationship.

Conflict Resolution

At some point, all relationships experience conflict. Conflict and difference of opinion are inescapable parts of life. We have negative feelings about the word "conflict." However, conflict can be the greatest motive for innovation and has been the catalyst for many inventions and technological breakthroughs. Conflict should not be avoided but should be guided to produce acceptable results. The challenge for a project manager is to use the conflict constructively and improve relationships with the customer.

> *The challenge for a project manager is to use the conflict constructively and improve relationships with the customer.*

Given that the project vision is understood and the customer's expectations are clear, how do the customer representative and project manager reach a win-win solution in areas of conflict? The following nine guidelines can help.

1. **Avoid Placing Blame.** This is the critical first step of conflict resolution. As project manager, you must accept that you are personally concerned with the situation and take responsibility for your actions. Therefore, blaming the conflict on someone else is unacceptable. The customer should be aware that you disagree with their position or actions. The usual way of saying, "Why did you do X?" is not appropriate, because it affixes blame, which will inhibit the conflict resolution process. In short, start with "I" not "you," avoid placing blame, and take ownership of your feelings and concerns. For example, saying, "I am concerned about our ability to meet your expectations," will be much more likely to create an opening for positive dialogue than saying, "Your expectations are not realistic."

   The second important item is to emphasize resolution when approaching the situation. A nonthreatening question such as, "When can we get together and see if we can resolve X?" starts the conflict resolution process on the correct path.

   Finally, you must enlist the customer's assistance. A question such as, "Can we agree to work together on this?" will frame a collaborative approach to resolving the problem, rather than trying to allocate blame.

2. **Clarify and Define the Issue.** Often conflict is a difference in perception rather than a difference of opinion or interest. Therefore, the second step, clarifying and defining the issue, ensures that the conflict is real. Use language that helps ensure mutual understanding of the problem such as, "Here's how I see the problem," and, "What do you think?"

3. **Listen Completely to the Other Party.** The customer representative must completely explain how he or she sees the problem. You must listen intently. Do not interrupt, but wait until the customer representative stops before seeking clarification. If necessary, paraphrase what you have been told to make sure he or she knows you understand. Be sure you fully understand the customer's point of view before moving on.

4. **State Your Point of View Clearly.** Now it is your turn to give your version of the problem. Be straightforward, admit your biases, be clear. Ask the customer representative not to interrupt you. When finished, ask them to paraphrase your viewpoint. Again, do not interrupt, but make sure the other person has fully understood your position.

5. **Work on What You Can Agree on.** Now you are ready to attempt to isolate the actual areas of disagreement. You can do this by jointly defining areas of the problem you agree on. This agreement leads you to develop mutually acceptable statements such as, "What we both want is . . . ," or, "We will both be satisfied when . . . ." These statements lead to the next guideline — brainstorm alternative solutions — which answers the question, "How are we going to get there?"

6. **Brainstorm Alternative Solutions.** By now most of the tension should be out of the situation, and the customer representative will be ready to create some mutually acceptable solutions. As with all brainstorming, do not be judgmental — let the ideas come out. If much tension remains, use more active listening to get at the cause of the tension.

7. **Attempt to Agree on a Potential Solution.** Now try to reach agreement on a potential solution. Write it down, leave it for a period, and come back to it. Whatever you decide, it is important to specify a time frame in which the potential solution should be tested.

8. **Document the Agreement.** Memorialize the solution, and communicate it to stakeholders and team members.

9. **Agree on How to Check if the Solution is Working.** The final task is to develop a way to measure how well your solution is working. It may require you to develop new measures. If you do, you will need to set some expectations of performance and also a time frame for judging the success of the solution.

Keep in mind that, initially, a certain amount of discomfort will need to be dealt with. A few practice conversations in the project manager's mind will help, but it is natural to be nervous. However, project managers should not use their nervousness as an excuse for not addressing the issue. The next time you deal with the issue will be that much more difficult, and the customer representative will be that much more entrenched in his or her position.

Summary

The customer relationship is successful when the customer is satisfied with the final product and with the services provided.

Relationship building is a fundamental part of leadership and essential to gaining the long-term trust and confidence of customers. The customer relationship is successful when the customer is satisfied with the final product and with the services provided. Ensuring a successful relationship means structuring the relationship between the project manager and the customer; understanding the customer's needs, expectations, strengths, and weaknesses; reinforcing the relationship with customer service; communicating with the customer; and maintaining a good relationship during difficult times. In today's competitive environment, strong relationships between project manager and customer are often the competitive edge that captures opportunity.

Other Resources

Block, Peter. 1994. *Stewardship: Choosing Service Over Self-Interest.* San Francisco: Berrett-Koehler.

Cross, Richard, and Janet Smith. 1995. *Customer Bonding: Pathway to Lasting Customer Loyalty.* Lincolnwood, IL: NTC Business Books.

Heskett, James; W. Earl Sasser, Jr.; and Christopher Hart. 1990. *Service Breakthroughs: Changing the Rules of the Game.* New York: Doubleday.

Peppers, Don, and Martha Rogers. 1993. *The One to One Future.* New York: Doubleday.

Stasiowski, Frank. 1993. *Value Pricing for the Design Firm.* New York: John Wiley.

Charter Team

OVERVIEW

Project planning is the single most important activity that will influence the success of the project. In CH2M HILL's project delivery process, planning is divided into three essential components: charter team, plan project, and endorse project.

This monograph focuses on the first of the planning activities — chartering the project team — but also discusses other aspects of team development, including building and sustaining the team. This monograph provides the project manager with a comprehensive view of how team synergy can add value to the project, the customer, and the enterprise.

Introduction

Project delivery is a team activity. Teaming builds flexibility and creativity into the way in which work can be performed and, for this reason, can greatly increase an enterprise's capability to deliver value-added projects to the customer.

This monograph overviews the effective use of teams as an approach to project delivery and offers rationales and guidelines for team development, a process that consists of chartering, building, and sustaining the project team.

What Is a Project Team?

A team is a group of people who work for a common purpose to produce a specific outcome.

A team is a group of people who work for a common purpose to produce a specific outcome. In project delivery, the project team consists of the project manager and the key staff. This team will use a standard set of processes in order to develop and deliver the desired products and services.

The project manager is responsible for *chartering* the team, *building* it into an effective work system, and *sustaining* a high level of team performance throughout the project.

The key staff are responsible for ensuring that all of the work necessary to meet the customer's expectations is performed. For small projects, the key staff may have sole responsibility for achieving project deliverables. For large projects, any number of additional subteams may be formed to deliver specific components of the overall project. The steps of team development are consistent, regardless of the size of the team or the type of project.

The project manager must decide how and when to involve the customer and other stakeholders in project team tasks and processes. In partnering, customer staff and enterprise staff form a single, integrated project team. Even though the customer is not a member of the enterprise's project team, customer representatives are part of a broader definition of a team, and they may be involved in certain functions and activities.

When Are Project Teams Required?

For the simplest project, the project manager designs the project, executes the work, and personally ensures the customer's satisfaction. In this case, the project manager is the manager, the technical expert, and the primary doer of the work.

However, as projects grow in size, scope, and complexity, the project manager must rely on others to perform more of the work and make day-to-day decisions that may have implications far beyond their apparent scope. A project team is essential when any one or more of the following conditions prevail:

- The project is too complex for any one person to be able to know and handle all the variables.

- The interdependencies of the project tasks are complex and are essential to overall project success.

- The project's requirements (schedule, budget, performance criteria) are such that commitment to all the goals by all the team members is essential if the project is to meet the customer's needs and expectations.

- The expertise required for successful project performance is spread among several key individuals. The collective knowledge and wisdom of these individuals are needed to ensure project success.

Under any of these circumstances, the project manager will be hard pressed to meet the project goals by working alone or by attempting to serve as the single point of knowledge or decision-making. Many people must contribute to the process and add their expertise with a full commitment to the agreed-upon goals of the project.

Selecting and Recruiting Team Members

Although the emphasis of this monograph is on managing the team after it has been formed, a brief discussion of selecting and recruiting team members is appropriate, because the project manager's ability to charter, build, and sustain team members will depend on the selected individuals.

The makeup of a team is highly dependent on the specific goals and expectations of the customer.

The makeup of a team is highly dependent on the specific goals and expectations of the customer. The request for proposals provides an initial sense of what the customer wants, and further discussions with the customer help to define the priorities in more detail. During the initial stage of a project, the project manager must determine the critical elements of the project and make staffing decisions based on this assessment.

The strategic nature of the project to the enterprise may influence the availability of resources to the project. A project of strategic value — one that will strengthen the enterprise's reputation, has the potential for additional work, or is highly visible — may facilitate access to personnel who are otherwise difficult to obtain, because they are geographically remote or are committed to other projects.

Although top experts in every relevant field may not be available, the project manager should always try to recruit the best qualified people at the appropriate skill level. In selecting individual members, the project manager must seek to balance the strengths and limitations of the members. Less experienced personnel may be fully capable of completing the assigned work and can be assisted by senior staff. Hiring for specific positions and using subcontractors are other options for filling vacancies in the staff, particularly on larger projects.

Most likely, the individuals selected for the team will not have previously worked together or will not have all of the required skills. Even if the project manager can recruit a dream team, specific steps will need to be taken to ensure that the team works well together and that individuals perform effectively on this project.

The Stages of Team Development

In order for a group of people to become a team and achieve the synergy that can result from effective teamwork, the following critical success factors must be in place:

- A common, agreed-upon set of goals, measures, and rules

- A commitment to the required goals and tasks and to each other

- Interdependent work: each person's work linked to the others

- Collective and individual accountabilities

- Acceptable team behaviors

- Adequate resources to perform the work as a team

To attain these factors, the project manager must have a basic understanding of the process that teams go through in their development (Figure 6). The stages of team development are chartering, building, and sustaining, and the phases are forming, storming, norming, performing, and excelling. The stages of team development are the main topic of this monograph and are discussed in detail after a brief discussion of the five phases of team development.

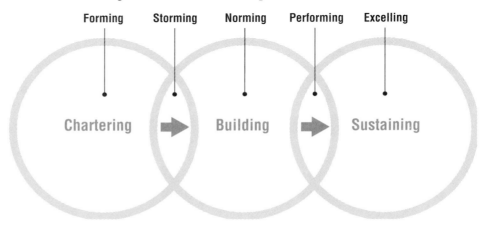

Figure 6. Team Development Process

Forming. Forming is the coming-together phase and is usually not confrontational because people are waiting to see how situations might develop. Activities include orientation meetings, which are typically directed by the project manager.

Storming. The storming phase is often marked by frustration and conflict as team members support their positions and points of view. Conflicts may occur as team members try to establish their status, responsibilities, and relative power and authority, and their relationship to the decision-making process. Attempts at this phase to create procedures and guidelines for team behavior may only be partially successful.

Norming. During the norming phase, leadership emerges, functional relationships develop, and conflicts that may have developed during the storming phase are resolved. Effective decision-making processes are established, and team members put their energy into the goals of the team.

Performing and Excelling. In the performing and excelling phases, collaboration among team members and high-quality performance become common, and team members trust one another and support the leadership.

The length and complexity of each of these phases is a function of the complexity of the roles and responsibilities of the team as well as the number of team members and their social styles and personal agendas. A relatively small project, requiring four or five people part-time for several months, would move quickly through these phases. A complex, multi-year, large-scale project with a number of full-time personnel would require much more attention from the project manager to the development process.

Stage One: Chartering the Team

Chartering a team may best be described as the ounce of prevention that is worth a pound of cure. Simply stated, chartering is the act of guiding a team through the process of defining itself: its purpose, scope, goals, roles, responsibilities, behaviors, and other elements that give a team the clarity of purpose essential for high-quality performance.

Chartering is the act of guiding a team through the process of defining itself.

The term "charter" is borrowed from the British sovereign system, where the king or queen granted, or chartered, certain rights or privileges on an individual. These privileges were often in the form of property and the right to own it, farm it, and govern it in exchange for a percentage of the profits from the land or a tax.

Today, the concept of chartering a team in an organization has a similar meaning. The organization confers certain authorities and resources to the team and team members. This authority has a defined boundary and scope of work. In return for this authority, the team is responsible for generating certain results. The definition of the purpose, scope, goals, behaviors, and roles and relationships of the team is the chartering process; the written description of these definitions is the project team charter.

In the project delivery process, chartering is one of three components of the planning phase (the other two are development of the workplan and endorsement of the project). Chartering occurs after the general parameters of the project have been defined, but before detailed development of the workplan. During the chartering process, the team will begin to address several important matters that will serve as input into the workplan, including project purpose, mission, and vision; measures of success; roles and responsibilities; and operating guidelines needed to help ensure effective communication and decision-making during subsequent project planning and execution activities. By engaging team members in this work, the project manager is, in effect, helping to build a well-aligned, focused, high-performance project team.

A chartering session should replace the traditional kickoff meeting.

The project manager and team members must be involved in the chartering process, but others may also be included. For example, the chartering could be sequenced to have the customer attend the initial session, where project parameters are presented and the charter is established. Then, the team could have a separate session to work through the details of the charter on its own, which would be followed by a final session, where the customer returns for a presentation and endorsement of the charter by all stakeholders.

The Benefits of Chartering

The primary benefits of chartering are threefold:

- Increases the probability that the team will be successful and will achieve high-quality performance

- Empowers team members, maximizing their effectiveness and influence

- Monitors team performance so that members can diagnose problems and take corrective actions

Chartering to Achieve High-Quality Performance

Teams commonly go astray or fail to perform as originally hoped. When the problems are analyzed, they are often related to a number of common issues: lack of a clear goal, lack of initial agreement regarding the purpose of the team, individual agendas overriding team goals, interpersonal conflicts, lack of resources, or unclear expectations. When an effort is made to identify the sources of these problems, it is often the case that these issues were never clarified at the beginning of the project, and the team started the project with the seeds of its poor performance or dysfunctionality already sown.

Chartering ensures that the team members share the same vision for the project.

Chartering ensures that team members share the same vision for the project, which greatly increases the probability that the team will experience both success and high-quality performance. Chartering is the basis for creating team behaviors that are stronger than individual behaviors. Chartering establishes the operating guidelines that govern team and individual behaviors. Chartering sets the stage for success.

Chartering for Empowerment

Empowerment is derived from the root word "power." Traditionally, power in organizations implies formal authority and control. To have power is to have the formal authority to commit resources, to delegate tasks, and to control events.

However, in a team-oriented environment, power has a different meaning. It is the ability to influence others or events and to create a situation in which others choose to behave in a certain way or make certain decisions. Individuals with power may have little or no formal authority in the organization. Yet, through their personal influence, logical persuasion, competence, strength of personality, or the respect they are given by others, they can influence behaviors and outcomes. These individuals are empowered.

Teams that are properly chartered are empowered teams. They have well-defined roles, responsibilities, boundaries, and pathways through the organization. The process by which they can freely operate is clarified through the charter. Similarly, the process by which they can bring their recommendations, decisions, or results to the organization is well defined. Although they may not have control over the formal and final decision-making process, they do have the ability to influence outcomes. Thus, chartered teams are empowered teams. The members of these teams know what they may decide, what they may recommend, and how both the decision and recommendation processes are implemented. Through this awareness, the effectiveness and influence of the team are maximized.

According to Stephen R. Covey (1992), in any work setting the staff are empowered when they have been given a clear understanding of the following:

- Desired results
- Parameters within which the results are to be accomplished
- Resources available to help achieve the desired results

- Expected standards of performance
- Consequences associated with various levels of performance

By this definition, chartering is a means of empowering team members, both individually and collectively. Chartering defines the overall project purpose as well as the expected contributions from each member. Performance measures are established; methods for managing work processes are clarified; and operating guidelines are set, indicating desired standards of conduct.

Chartering to Monitor Performance

Effective chartering can be so powerful that it goes beyond its core goal of defining the vision, purpose, mission, roles, relationships, and behaviors of the team and its members. The most effective high-performance teams have a sound and well-developed charter that is so strong that it enables other important activities to occur. First, the charter contains a baseline against which the team can assess its performance on an ongoing basis. Thus, high-performance teams know when they are not achieving at their desired level. Second, since the charter describes the behaviors and activities required for successful performance, teams recognize when they are faltering and can implement the self-correcting mechanisms that enable them to resolve their problems and return to high-quality performance. The charter provides the foundation essential for monitoring performance, diagnosing problems, and evaluating and implementing solutions.

Elements of a Team Charter

The contents of a charter will vary based on the nature of the team, the nature of the work to be performed, the complexity and length of the work to be performed, and other factors internal and external to the enterprise. However, certain elements of a charter are essential for any team to have a successful chartering process. Other additional charter elements are included, based on the conditions under which the team is functioning.

Essential Charter Elements

Following is a list of the essential elements of a charter with a definition and brief description of each.

Vision. The vision is a statement of the larger purpose of the project. The vision statement answers the question, "Why does this project exist?" Preferably, it will be framed in terms of the future state that exists as a result of the project. For example, the vision of a project might be enhanced access to public transportation for all citizens in our community. If the project vision is clearly defined, then the chartering can move directly to defining the purpose.

Purpose. The purpose for a team answers the questions: "Why does this team exist?" "Why was it formed?" "What is it expected to do?" The purpose should be clearly stated in a single sentence or short paragraph. The purpose is typically derived from the project definition as it appears in the contract and is closely linked to the project vision.

Membership. Membership is not just providing expertise when requested or participating in one or several meetings. Membership carries with it defined responsibilities and a degree of commitment to the team and to the other team members. Membership must be clear: individuals must know when they are on a team and what the scope of their membership is in terms of roles, responsibilities, and length of commitment.

Mission. The mission is commonly an extension of the team's purpose. It expands on the purpose, often with a broadly measurable result. For example, a team may be established with the purpose of consulting on a long-term master planning process for a municipal water authority. The team may subsequently develop a more specific mission of conducting a preliminary assessment of the existing master plan by a specified date.

Organizational Linkage. The organizational linkage is a description of the formal link between the team and the enterprise, which answers the questions: "To whom does the team report?" "Is the team part of a formal structure?" "How does the team relate to that structure?" "How is it linked for purposes of resources, communication, authority, and approval?"

Boundaries. Describing the boundaries is a critical element of the charter and an area often left unclear. The boundaries define the scope of the project team's formal authority or what it may do without permission. The boundaries also define the area of influence or what it may do with permission. The boundaries describe shared responsibilities or areas in which team members are expected to initiate action to support others. The boundaries also define the limits of the project team's authority; for example, decisions it may not make, resources it may not expend, commitments it may not exceed. The management of the project team and the enterprise jointly define the boundaries.

Team and Individual Responsibilities. A team has a defined scope of primary responsibility. These responsibilities are held by the entire team, and each team member is equally responsible for their attainment. In addition to these team responsibilities, each team member has individual responsibilities. Overall team responsibilities are typically reviewed and measured by individuals who can represent the customer and the enterprise's management. Individual team member responsibilities are typically reviewed and measured internally by the project manager and other team members. The criteria described below are the means by which the achievement of the team and individual responsibilities are measured.

Measures of Success. Every team should be provided with the greatest opportunity to experience success. Success, however, must not be subjective or unclear. Success must be defined in terms of specific results that are measurable against agreed-upon criteria. Measures of success may be established in terms of quantity, quality, time, cost, or a combination of these criteria. The greater the clarity of the criteria, the greater the probability that the team members, individually and collectively, will achieve them.

Operating Guidelines. The operating guidelines describe how the team will govern itself. Guidelines are created to answer questions such as how the team will make decisions; how it will communicate internally and externally (see Virtual Teaming on page 76); how it will resolve conflict and; how it will manage change. By creating operating guidelines prior to the implementation of detailed tasks, many potential problems can be avoided. Many of these operating guidelines will become the basis for certain workplan elements, for example, the instructions and the communications plan.

Additional Charter Elements

In addition to the essential elements described above, a charter may contain a number of additional elements. Depending on the scope and length of the team's mission, the nature of the team's work, and the team's relationship to the enterprise, these elements may or may not be essential; however, they should be considered and used if they are appropriate for the project team and will contribute to the project's successful implementation. Following is a short description of each of these additional elements.

The contents of a charter will depend on the specifics of a project.

Organizational Priorities. Since any project is only one of many endeavors through which the enterprise is attempting to realize its overall mission and vision, a declaration of just what these larger corporate aims are may provide a useful context for the project team. This can be accomplished, for example, through an understanding of the strategic implications and opportunities that will result from the success of the project. The same is true of the customer: knowledge of where the project fits within the larger scheme of the customer's organization can be of immense value to the team.

Critical Success Factors. Project-specific critical success factors include the performance factors most crucial to successful completion of the project. In other words, what are the vital aspects of the project that the team absolutely must not fail at with respect to customer relations, team performance, project planning, and project execution. Most teams identify between three and seven critical success factors and then develop performance measures that can be used to determine the performance of each factor.

Shared Responsibilities. In addition to team members identifying their individual responsibilities (see Essential Charter Elements, page 72), they should also identify the areas in which their own work is interdependent with that of other persons, within and outside the team. In the lexicon of *quality improvement*, all those whom the individual must depend on are called *suppliers*, and those who, in turn, depend on the individual are *customers*. However these relationships are configured, it is important to elicit among all the team members a sense of shared purpose. A shared purpose gives individual team members a vested interest in the success of other team members and therefore encourages collaboration.

Virtual Teaming

On all but the largest projects, the customer and project team members will probably not have full-time, face-to-face availability with one another. More likely, they will be communicating with each other over a variety of electronic media, including telephone, fax, internet, and e-mail. In this kind of environment, it is doubly important to ensure that the team is adequately chartered and that the charter is well understood by all. Charles Handy (1995) suggests that "the more virtual an organization becomes, the more its people need to meet in person" and get to know each other.

The electronic systems must be topnotch, capable of providing full and timely service to all members of the team. And the systems must be used. This often means ensuring that each member has a basic level of fluency with each electronic medium and the necessary hardware and software.

The protocol for use of electronic media should allow for both formal and informal types of communication. With this flexibility, users will need to be clear which type of message they are sending.

Communication in the virtual team should occur as often as needed, and routine updates and sharing of documents between computers should occur at least once a week with a follow-up telephone conference call. Face-to-face meetings should occur whenever possible and should have time built into the agenda for developing relationships.

Core Values. Project teams may want to use the enterprise's core values to help steer the development of guiding principles and operating guidelines.

Examples of these core values include the following:

- Honesty, integrity, and trust
- Responsive customer focus
- Emphasis on people
- Continuous improvement
- Quest for innovation
- Community commitment

Guiding Principles. Guiding principles are statements derived from commonly held team values, describing appropriate and inappropriate behaviors. Some examples follow:

- Respect for each other is critical to the team's success.
- Customer needs come first.
- No actions will be taken that will increase our profit at the expense of another party.

Rules of Interpersonal Conduct. Building on the guiding principles, the rules of interpersonal conduct establish specific rules for team members' behaviors in project-related activities.

Protocol for Resolving Interpersonal Conflict. Again, building on guiding principles and on operating guidelines for decision-making, project managers can establish a protocol for resolving interpersonal conflict. This protocol usually includes a general acknowledgment that conflicts are probable during a project, a set of procedures for classifying and treating disagreements, and identification of the parties who will take primary responsibility for resolving various types of conflict.

The Chartering Process

The essential and additional charter elements described above can be categorized into a five-step process that can be followed to develop the charter. These steps and the associated chartering elements follow:

1. Define the team.
   - Vision
   - Purpose
   - Boundaries
   - Organizational linkage

2. Clarify the team purpose.
   - Membership
   - Mission
   - Measures of success
   - Organizational priorities
   - Critical success factors

3. Define responsibilities.
   - Team and individual responsibilities
   - Shared responsibilities

4. Develop team operating guidelines.

5. Develop interpersonal behavior guidelines.
   - Core values
   - Guiding principles
   - Rules of interpersonal conduct
   - Protocol for resolving interpersonal conflict

Once the essential and additional charter elements have been prepared, the charter must be endorsed by the stakeholders. (See the monograph *Endorse Project*.) Endorsement means both the approval of the charter and the workplan and the ongoing commitment to support them. Once the charter has been endorsed, it should be shared with all stakeholders. This contributes to a shared project understanding and an open, communicative relationship.

Stage Two: Building the Team

Team building begins after the team has been chartered. In this stage, training and ongoing skill development are interwoven with the team's project work, and attention is paid to the quality of the team's work. A variety of methods and tools are available in the literature to address total quality and team building (Burke 1987, Dyer 1977, Marshall 1995, Resnick 1994, Stack 1992).

Four major areas of skill development should be the focus of this phase of team development: problem-solving skills, process improvement skills, interpersonal skills, and decision-making skills.

Problem-Solving Skills

Attention should be paid to understanding and developing problem-solving skills. In order to function effectively, teams need to be able to identify and resolve problems that will be encountered in delivering the project. Some problems will arise in relation to the deliverables, while others will stem from the team itself.

Methods and tools for achieving total quality should be applied during the building stage of team development. If these methods and tools are applied to the project, they can add value to the project and improve team members' problem-solving skills. Although they are beyond the scope of this monograph, tools such as affinity diagramming, tree diagramming, cause and effect analysis, data gathering and analysis methodologies, and prioritization matrixes are examples of techniques that can be used to expand our problem-solving skills.

Process Improvement Skills

Although a charter and project workplan (See the monograph *Developing the Workplan*) may appear to be complete when they are first generated, inconsistencies, redundancies, and other flaws in the work processes described in these documents are likely to surface as they are translated into day-to-day activities. Therefore, process improvement is an essential part of the team's work during implementation. When problems occur, work processes should be carefully analyzed to identify which activities are not adding value to the project and how they are affecting productivity and customer satisfaction. Where problems exist, improvements are suggested and tested to see if the process can be improved.

Interpersonal Skills

Interpersonal skill development or training may be necessary for team members when conflict arises.

If any team member does not have a positive relationship with the customer or his or her behavior does not add to the synergy of the team, the building stage is where these skills should be developed. Training on social styles is valuable and can be useful in developing customer relationships throughout this stage of team development. (See the monograph *Customer Relationships*.) If a conflict develops between two team members or between a team member and a customer representative, the specific problem should be solved, and conflict-resolution training should be provided for the involved team members.

For team synergy to occur, certain rules of conduct must be followed. If these rules are violated, teams may develop disruptive behavior and become dysfunctional. For this reason, a new team should examine these rules of conduct, modify or add to them as appropriate for the team's circumstances, and then monitor its behavior against these rules. Teams can analyze their behavior against the following recommended rules of conduct and apply both individual and team feedback for continuous improvement:

- Make team goals the highest priority, not individual or personal goals.

- Check jobs at the meeting room door; no positional behavior.

- Base decisions on what is right, not who is right.

- Contribute and listen to the contributions of others; no inequality among team members.

- Contribute with flexibility; no fixed positions.

- Make decisions based on fact, analysis, and good judgment, not opinion.

- Make decisions openly, not at off-line negotiations.

- Consider that perfection can be the enemy of the common good.

- Strive for consensus, not unanimity; the right of infinite refusal is unacceptable.

- Know and accept when the project manager must make the decision.

Decision-Making Skills

Problem solving will help the team identify whether a problem is due to a particular situation or certain team member behaviors or both. In order to develop and implement an appropriate response, the team will need to have effective decision-making skills.

Because teams often try to use consensus decision-making, many project managers come to the following incorrect conclusions:

- All decisions should be made by the entire team.

- Team decision-making should always use a consensus-building style.

- As long as one team member disagrees, consensus has not been reached.

- The project manager should give up his or her authority to the team process.

- If consensus cannot be reached, a team vote is the second best alternative.

These myths have created more team problems and led to more poor decisions than can be imagined. The following guidelines replace the myths stated above with a more viable set of principles to help govern the project team decision-making process:

The project manager is responsible for selecting the decision-making process that is appropriate to the situation.

- The project manager is the team leader. In this capacity, the project manager is responsible for selecting the decision-making process that is appropriate to the situation. The project manager is also ultimately responsible for all decisions, regardless of who made them or how they were made.

- The general guidelines for decision-making at all levels — who makes what kinds of decisions and under what conditions — should have been agreed on during the team chartering process.

- The project manager should communicate to the project team what decision-making strategy is being used. For example, if the project manager is asking for input but will make the decision, then the team members should understand that their input does not constitute a formal vote and is not part of a consensus-building process.

- The project manager may delegate the decision-making or request a recommendation and retain the right to make the final decision. This assignment may be given to an individual or a group. In this case, the project manager must let the individual or group know in advance whether they should actually make the decision and act on it or whether they should return with a recommendation to the project manager.

- If the project manager elects to keep the authority for decision-making, he or she should let the team know whether the decision is:

    - One-on-none: The project manager will decide alone.

    - One-on-one: The project manager will decide with input from one other defined person.

    - One-on-some: The project manager will decide with the input of a defined subgroup.

    - One-on-all: The project manager will decide with the input of the entire team.

Consensus is the best decision-making strategy to use only under several defined circumstances:

- The team has no particular expert who is best qualified to make the decision.

- The team has no defined answer, and the entire team can add value to the process.

- The team needs a creative solution.

- The entire team is committed to the decision, and implementation of the decision is essential.

Under these circumstances, the time and energy spent in the consensus-building process is well worth the investment. If consensus cannot be reached, the project manager should make the decision. This approach is a superior alternative to voting by the team.

Stage Three: Sustaining the Team

As project work continues to expand in scope and complexity, the project manager will increasingly be called on to serve in the role of team leader, the most important role that the project manager must fulfill. (See the monograph *Roles and Responsibilities of the Project Manager.*) With a high-performance, synergistic team, a project manager can achieve the results demanded by an increasingly competitive environment.

High performance means that a team is able to optimize the technical and behavioral facets of its work.

The third stage of development, sustaining the project team, is critical if the team is to become a high-performance team. High performance means that a team is able to optimize the technical and behavioral facets of its work; that is, the right people are performing the right tasks in the right way at the right time. Achieving this level of performance usually requires experience, along with a commitment to continuous improvement, and is therefore a part of the team's ongoing development after basic work processes have been established and tested.

The difference between teams that perform adequately and those that ultimately achieve high performance is based on the team's ability to recognize when it is not performing well, analyze the situation without blame, and take corrective action. To achieve this level of performance, the team must develop its capabilities in three areas: diagnosis, evaluation and feedback, and corrective action.

Diagnosis of Team Performance

Diagnostic skills are necessary to measure: (1) performance against project goals and expectations; (2) the team members' contributions to meeting these goals and expectations; and (3) the customer relationship and its evolution towards stronger professional, personal, and organizational relationships.

When a project team is not performing well, there are many possible causes. Without attempting to be simplistic in this analysis, the project manager should first examine the team charter. Is it complete? Is it fully endorsed by the team? If not, the missing elements or lack of endorsement are likely the culprit for poor team performance and represent a good place to start the evaluation.

Poor performance may require a diagnosis of the charter, team behavior, the external project environment, and the team makeup.

If the charter is complete, a second area of diagnosis is team behavior and the underlying reasons for that behavior. The metaphor of the team as an iceberg is a valuable one in understanding the true nature of the team (see The Team Iceberg, page 89). In the team iceberg, most of the iceberg lies below the water line.

The visible part of the team iceberg — interpersonal relationships and behaviors — is often perceived to be the cause of the team's problem. More often, however, the cause of the team's problem lies below the water line. In determining the cause of a problem, the project manager should ask certain questions:

- Are the goals and purposes of the team clear?

- Are collective and individual roles well defined?

- Are the work processes and operating guidelines well articulated and are they being used as agreed?

- Is inappropriate interpersonal behavior interfering with team performance?

If a team member consistently demonstrates behavior that detracts from rather than adds to team performance, then the project manager must take action as part of his or her role as the team leader. This action may be private, such as a one-on-one discussion with the team member. It may be facilitated through an indirect group process, such as a team-building activity, or conducted through a direct group process, such as a round-table feedback session. In the most extreme case, the project manager will need to remove that person from the team.

A third element to consider in the diagnosis is the external project environment. If the team performed well in the past but team performance has declined, something may have changed in the external environment. These changes could be in conflict with the original project charter or workplan. If this is the case, then either the charter or workplan should be modified to address the changes in the external environment, redefining the conditions for success.

The fourth possible area to diagnose is the composition of the team itself. Do the team members have the experience, skill set, and knowledge needed to perform the work? If not, this flaw must be corrected rapidly. Correction can be made by recruiting additional team members, hiring temporary subconsultants, or building the knowledge or skills needed by team members. The project manager may need to take difficult measures, such as replacing team members, to ensure project success and a satisfied customer.

Evaluation and Feedback

After diagnosis, high-performance teams evaluate the cause of the problem, then give and receive feedback in a nonjudgmental manner so that improvements can be made. This feedback is individual and interpersonal, as well as team related. High-performance teams also know how to receive feedback from and provide feedback to the customer in a way that both improves the situation and adds value to the customer relationship.

Feedback on individual and collective performances should be provided at regular intervals.

The project manager will need to serve as a coach and mentor during this phase of the team's growth. Feedback on individual and collective performances should be provided at regular intervals.

Corrective Action

Corrective action at the individual and team levels is the third set of capabilities essential for sustaining the team. A specific action may be technical in nature or it may be personal or interpersonal. High-performance teams have the courage to take corrective action even when it is difficult, knowing that the action will ultimately create a better result for the project, the customer, and the enterprise.

The decision-making models already developed and tested by the team can now be used to develop effective corrective actions for most problems. The project manager retains final authority and responsibility, however, and must ensure that appropriate actions are taken.

Summary

In this monograph, we have described team development as an approach to effective project delivery. Methods and tools have been introduced to help the project manager, who is responsible for team development, address the various issues that will be encountered in chartering, building, and sustaining effective team performance. The steps in the chartering process lead to a charter that the team, the customer, the stakeholders, and the enterprise's management can endorse and actively support.

Strong, synergistic teams lead to strong project performance and satisfied customers. However, project team members must go through a process of defining themselves as they work toward becoming a strong team. Chartering is the process used to define the roles, responsibilities, and operating parameters for teams.

As teams are built and sustained, the chartering process provides the basis for applying diagnostic and evaluation tools to correct the dysfunctional behaviors that, if uncorrected, can lead to dysfunctional teams. Even when problems arise, strong teams that have been chartered can maintain their synergy through the skillful application of these tools.

The Team Iceberg

Just as an iceberg is largely below the water (only one eighth is thought to be above the water's surface) so, too, is the true nature of a team only partially visible.

When we first observe a team at work, we see the team members interact with other members and customer representatives. From observations of interpersonal relationships, we become aware of dysfunctional behavior if it exists. However, if we examine and react solely to dysfunctional behavior, which is visible above the surface, we are likely to miss the true causes of dysfunctional behavior: ineffective or undefined processes, roles, and goals.

In order to establish the basis for a high-performance team, we must address the issues as shown in the figure from the bottom of the iceberg up. The base of the iceberg, the foundation for team development, concerns the clarification of goals. Goals are created with varying levels of specificity. At the highest level, they are statements of vision and purpose. At the lowest level, they are specific measurable outcomes or accountabilities for the team and team members.

The second level of the iceberg concerns the clarification of team and individual roles and responsibilities, which are aligned with the project goals.

The third level of the iceberg consists of the development of team processes. Team processes describe the "how" of team operations. By clarifying processes, the team determines how it will communicate, meet, make decisions, resolve conflicts, and set priorities. These are the operating guidelines for a team, which define the parameters that govern acceptable team behavior.

Much of the work needed to address these three levels below the water line can be accomplished in the first stage of team development, the team chartering process.

Team Iceberg

Visible Interpersonal Relationships

"Water line" of Visible Team Behavior

Process
- Decision-making
- Issue Resolution
- Problem-solving
- Communications
- Planning
- Meeting Management

Roles
- Shared & Individual
- Primary & Secondary
- Conflict Free

Purpose & Goals
- Visionary & Inspiring
- Clear & Commonly Held
- Specific & Measurable

References

Burke, W. Warner. 1987. *Organization Development: A Normative View.* Reading, MA: Addison-Wesley.

Covey, Stephen R. 1992. *Principle-Centered Leadership.* New York: Simon & Schuster.

Dyer, William. 1977. *Team Building: Issues and Alternatives.* Reading, MA: Addison-Wesley.

Handy, Charles. 1995. "Trust and the Virtual Organization." *Harvard Business Review*, May-June: 40-50.

Marshall, Edward M. 1995. *Transforming the Way We Work: The Power of the Collaborative Workplace.* NY: AMACOM.

Resnick, Harold. 1994. *Business Process Reengineering.* Marlborough, MA: Work Systems Associates, Inc.

Stack, Jack. 1992. *The Great Game of Business.* New York: Currency Doubleday.

Plan Project

Developing the workplan is step two in the planning phase of the project delivery system. Workplan development roughly follows team chartering and precedes team endorsement.

The workplan is a collection of documents that communicates essential information about a project to everyone who is involved in the project. It provides the marching orders for the team, and if properly developed and endorsed by the team, the customer, and other involved stakeholders, the workplan will pave the road to successful project completion.

This monograph covers the benefits of developing a workplan, answers some of the most commonly asked questions that project managers have about developing workplans, and describes the essential and optional elements of a workplan, which should be tailored to your project's specific needs.

Introduction

Planning the project is the single most important activity that will influence the project, because successful project execution is not possible without a good plan.

The project workplan describes the focused application of the knowledge, skills, tools, and processes that the project team will use to meet or exceed the customer's requirements for a project. The project workplan becomes a powerful force for creating a high-quality project and having a satisfied customer.

In this monograph, the results of many collective years of experience are presented to illustrate how a project manager accomplishes the workplanning component of the project delivery process.

The Workplan Defined

An oft-quoted Chinese proverb says that one picture is worth a thousand words. The project workplan is that picture — your most valuable communication tool. A project workplan is a collection of documents that communicates essential information about a project to everyone who is involved in the project. It does not have to be lengthy, but it must address all necessary aspects of completing the project from start to finish. Good workplans contain minimal text, including only the information required to clearly define the subject. Good workplans make maximum use of graphics and reference standardized procedures wherever possible.

As a project manager, you are charged with the responsibility of developing the workplan, gaining endorsement of the project team, and updating the workplan as necessary to ensure that the final project meets or exceeds the customer's expectations.

The objective in project workplanning is to clearly define, for all who will become involved in completing the project, the information they need to work together as a team. No project should ever enter its execution phase without a project workplan that has been created and endorsed by the project stakeholders. In the absence of a good workplan, a quality project is impossible and the customer will be dissatisfied.

Workplan Benefits

Many of the benefits attributable to workplanning are obvious. We can easily understand that the workplanning process will help the team understand what is to be accomplished and who will do the work. Just as obvious are the benefits of scheduling activities and the cost savings possible through avoiding blind alleys and throwaway work. Similarly, we all have experienced miscommunications with others and can easily understand the importance of concise but thorough communication, which helps to ensure that the customer and the enterprise share the same expectations for the project.

Aside from the obvious benefits of the workplan, it provides other, more subtle advantages. For example, when a workplan is created through a team effort, each team member tends to gain a high level of commitment to project success. Thus, the team tends to be cohesive and self-directed towards a quality outcome, and the members are more willing to put in extra effort when it is required because they understand the goals and what is needed to accomplish them.

Project managers who consistently plan well are much more likely to see their projects accomplished in an atmosphere of high morale than are those who do not plan well. And those who plan well are much more likely to experience rapid and satisfying career advancement. Even if there were no other benefits to good project workplanning than personal and corporate success, the process would still be valuable.

The workplan provides the project team's marching orders.

Development of the project workplan is essential because the workplan provides the project team's marching orders so that all team members can work together efficiently. Workplans are required for all projects, regardless of size and type. Even small projects, having only a few team members, will benefit from workplans because they disseminate vital information to all stakeholders in a timely fashion. Large projects, particularly those accomplished in multiple offices, are even more dependent on good workplans. The absence of uniform instructions provided in a workplan will cause quality deficiencies, cost overruns, schedule slippage, and morale problems among the project team members.

A structure can be built without a design plan, but the results are never optimal. Similarly, a project can be managed without a workplan, but the results are always inferior. Just as design plans communicate construction details to a builder, the project workplan communicates essential project information to all stakeholders. A good project workplan is fundamental to a successful project; successful projects are fundamental to the success of the project manager, to the success of the enterprise, and most importantly, to the satisfaction of the customer.

A Workplan's Essential Elements

Communication is the goal of workplanning. The project workplan is the tool that most efficiently allows all project stakeholders to understand essential project information and to commit themselves to the project. These essential elements answer the following questions:

- What needs to be done? Project definition

- Who is going to do the work and with what special equipment? Project resources

- When is the work going to be done? Project schedule

- How much is the work going to cost? Project budget

- How is the work going to be accomplished? Project instructions

- How will quality be ensured? Quality management plan

- How will the customer be kept satisfied? Customer service plan

- How will change be managed? Change management plan

- How will the project be closed? Closure plan

The goal of every project manager should be to disseminate the above information to all project stakeholders in an efficient, concise manner. Each of the above listed elements is described in detail after a discussion of the workplanning process.

The Workplanning Process: Commonly Asked Questions

Project managers typically raise a number of questions when learning how to develop workplans. Among the most common questions are the following:

- Who leads the workplan process?

- Who helps prepare the workplan?

- Who will use the workplan?

- When do I begin preparing a workplan?

- How much time will it take to prepare a workplan?

- What format should I use for the workplan?

- How will the workplan be used?

- How do I get stakeholders to endorse the workplan?

- When do I update the workplan?

Who Leads the Workplan Process?

As the project manager, you are responsible for understanding the customer's vision, needs, and expectations.

As the project manager, you are responsible for understanding the customer's vision, needs, and expectations; that is, you lead the workplanning process. Working with the project team, you incorporate the customer's vision, needs, and expectations into the workplan elements and ensure that the team meets or exceeds them. If you are unfamiliar with some of the workplanning elements, then seek help from more experienced project managers. Most project managers are eager to share their experience and offer assistance. Similarly, if you are a more experienced manager, help those who have little workplanning experience.

Who Helps Prepare the Workplan?

On small projects, the project manager will accomplish almost all of the initial planning with assistance from customer representatives and internal staff. Workplans from previous projects may be valuable as guides. These workplans may be available from the enterprise's project library or from project managers who have maintained personal files of previous projects. (If you are a beginning project manager, you should plan to save a copy of completed workplans.) Supervisory personnel can help locate project staff and assist with estimates based on experience, and planning software can provide labor rates for specific staff positions.

For large, complex projects, the project manager should divide the planning among key project team members. These team members may include assistant managers, lead staff, and design and construction managers — in short, any individual who will be working on the project in either a supervisory or unique technical role or who possesses experience or knowledge critical to the success of the project.

The team approach to workplanning yields buy-in during the planning phase.

Dividing the workplanning effort has the obvious advantage of spreading the work load, but it also has the advantage of drawing on the skills of a variety of people. The resulting team effort has been proven to yield superior results. Not only is the team-prepared workplan less likely to contain fatal flaws than does the "lone wolf" approach, but the workplan is almost always obtained more quickly and at a lower cost. A final advantage to the team approach to workplanning is that it yields team buy-in during the planning phase and this, in turn, engenders superior team performance and morale during the execution phase.

Who Will Use the Workplan?

Since the workplan constitutes the primary description of project people, products, and procedures, maximum benefit will be obtained if it is widely disseminated and continuously consulted by the project team, including the customer and key stakeholders. In terms of distribution, the project manager should print and distribute too many copies, rather than too few. Since the workplan will probably be revised, a distribution list should be kept in the project files so that revisions to the workplan can quickly and consistently be distributed. This distribution list should include the customer and project team members. In certain situations, third-party stakeholders will also need a copy.

The Customer

All too often, project managers do not share their workplans with the owner of the project: the customer. This is poor project management and difficult to justify considering the benefits that are derived from sharing these communications. For example, a documented description of how a project will be executed, including methods and resources, is vital to the customer's confidence in the project manager's understanding of the project and its objectives. Also, since the workplan identifies an agreed-upon level of effort to perform the work, surprises later on in the project are eliminated.

Good project managers include in the workplan, where appropriate, customer tasks, which show the customer how they will participate and how their participation will affect the project. Clearly identifying the customer's role in the workplan and gaining their endorsement of the workplan will contribute to their commitment to the project.

The customer may not want to review all of the details in your workplan, but at a minimum, the project manager should share those elements of greatest interest to the customer, such as the project definition, work breakdown structure, quality management plan, schedule, and customer service plan.

Project Team

The workplan should be distributed to the enterprise's project team, including staff who will benefit from using parts of the workplan, the project sponsor, and subcontractors or subconsultants.

Workplan Users

A user of the project workplan is any employee whose labor will be used to complete the project. It is easy to remember the key team members during the workplanning effort, but too often, supervisory and support staff are forgotten. One solution is to have an assigned individual responsible for ensuring that every project has a workplan and that it is properly distributed. This approach is quite beneficial: aside from the value of building a collection of workplan examples, it helps ensure that everyone is appropriately informed.

When project managers develop distribution lists for project workplans, they should remember the less obvious users, such as consultants (reviewers), accounting (billing instructions), purchasing, editing, word processing, graphics (particularly if software or standards are an issue), and the mail room if unusual purchases or shipping techniques are needed. Do not forget to give the receptionist a list of the key project team members, the key customer personnel who will be calling the office, and any project-related telephone or fax numbers and internet e-mail addresses. Remembering these individuals early in the project makes for better communication and is greatly appreciated by all who support your project.

Keep in mind that not everyone will need the entire project workplan. Do not waste money distributing information that people do not need. On the other hand, be sure everyone has access to the information they do need.

Project Sponsors

Project sponsors are senior individuals assigned to larger projects to support the project manager. They are responsible for reviewing and approving workplans and assisting the manager in procuring necessary resources. The sponsors are also mentors, helpers to the project manager during times of difficulty, and a link between the project manager and senior management. Project sponsors are to be given all workplan documents.

Subcontractors and/or Subconsultants

If the project team includes subconsultants to assist with project work, they have the same need for the project workplan as does the internal team. In such cases, provide them with complete, up-to-date copies of any referenced standards (except external standards, such as building codes). Subconsultants cannot be expected to follow required processes or procedures unless they are informed. If they are going to be expected to conform to the workplan, they must know what is expected.

When Do I Begin Preparing a Workplan?

In many cases, the preliminary workplanning effort begins during the project procurement phase. When competition for a project occurs, proposals introduce key project team members and illustrate project methodology to potential customers who short-list and, in some cases, select the enterprise based on the proposals. If a proposal has been submitted to a customer, its contents should be carefully checked during any follow-on planning activity. Proposals normally contain proposed rosters of key team members, rudimentary schedules, and suggested project approaches, including tasks and subtasks. For new projects, these tasks and subtasks should be entered into project planning software and an initial budget should be prepared for the proposed project. This preliminary planning will provide useful information to include in the project workplan.

The preliminary workplanning effort begins during the project procurement phase.

In other cases, the detailed workplanning effort may not begin in earnest until after a contract or agreement between the customer and the enterprise has been signed. In some cases, a long-standing contract may exist where professional services are requested by the customer on a task-order basis. In this case, the workplanning effort should probably begin with the drafting of the task order to ensure that an appropriate scope is agreed upon.

In any event, the best time to begin detailed project workplanning is as soon as tasks and sufficient resources (labor) can be identified, as soon as you generally know what the project entails, and as soon as one or more individuals are assigned to the project as staff. However, keep in mind that there is a significant difference between preliminary workplanning and detailed final workplanning. Preliminary workplanning makes sense early in a project. It is useful even if unknowns exist, and it is useful as a means of determining what those unknowns are. Finally, it is extremely valuable during negotiations, particularly when initial information is entered into project management software. On the other hand, detailed final planning for hypothetical scopes, schedules, or budgets is seldom cost-effective, because it almost always results in a significant amount of wasted effort: it is far better to plan just what you can than to have to "can" your plan.

As a project manager, you cannot be expected to possess a crystal ball or be a prophet. If a project is so nebulous that almost every element of a workplan is conjectural, that project should not be undertaken on a fixed-effort basis. In this case, a feasibility study or project definition study is appropriate. These studies are meant to test alternatives and constitute an early form of project planning. They are often done on a time-and-materials or best-effort basis. Workplanning for feasibility or project definition studies requires creating a scope statement that delineates what will and what will not be studied.

Project teams often change between the time a project is procured and the time project work is authorized to start. Particular attention must be given to preliminary planning if the project manager was not involved in the project procurement and contract negotiations. The wise project manager will make his or her own assessment of how the project should be accomplished, regardless of whether another manager has preplanned the work.

How Much Time Will It Take To Prepare a Workplan?

As a rule of thumb, the workplan for most reasonably well-defined projects can be completed and ready for endorsement with a resource expenditure of up to 30 percent of the overall project management budget. Project management itself may consume as much as 20 percent of the overall project labor budget, although the average is closer to 10 percent. Therefore, about 3 to 5 percent of the overall labor budget may be used to accomplish the initial planning. However, other than as a statistical median, project managers should not aim at a 3 percent target. Each project will be different; some will take more time, some less.

The time spent planning and organizing a project should increase in direct proportion to its size and complexity. Large projects and projects with extensive customer and stakeholder involvement usually require increased planning effort, including lengthy schedules; multiple, interdependent tasks in the work breakdown structure; and coordination of multidisciplinary staff working in multiple offices.

How then should a project manager decide on the level of effort to devote to the project workplan? When does the effort become counterproductive? The optimum planning effort occurs when the project workplan adequately communicates the necessary information. Anything more is "gold plate" and, although nice, is not necessary. Anything less should be tolerated only if project unknowns preclude completion with adequate detail. In this case, the plan should acknowledge omissions, commit to subsequent completion, and proceed on to the next planning activity.

Often, project information vital for planning is missing at project inception, including support staff names, intermediate project deadlines, milestones, and, in some cases, even project budget. In fact, the ultimate scope of some projects is not known until the initial workplan defines a probable budget for a preliminary yet specific scope that the customer can respond to. Then the customer can enlarge or reduce the project scope to reflect their financial resources.

What Format Should I Use for the Workplan?

Workplan format is relatively unimportant compared to workplan content. However, the workplan is the project manager's primary communication tool, and it should be simple, concise, legible, and logically organized. A fancy format adds little to a workplan's utility and often costs, or is perceived to cost, precious dollars. As long as the workplan conveys the intended information, any reasonable format is acceptable. Minimal text should be the objective: make maximum use of software-generated charts, tables, and figures, and reference standardized procedures whenever appropriate.

Whatever format is used, the workplan should contain a table of contents, which helps readers quickly overview the contents and navigate through the document. Also, project managers can review the contents to ensure that all of the workplan elements either have been included or have been intentionally excluded.

How Will the Workplan Be Used?

The workplan is an excellent tool for focusing team members on the entire project for the project's duration. If you bury the plan in some little-consulted corner of your project files, you will have certainly wasted your planning effort, and you will probably reinvent the wheel more than once by replanning what you have already planned. Keep the workplan handy, and consult it often. A workplan that is no longer being followed or updated is useless. So use the workplan often, and as aspects of the project change, update the workplan.

Likewise, use the methods that you committed to use in the workplan. Under no circumstance should you adopt new project procedures without appropriately revising the project workplan and communicating the changes to the customer, project team, and project sponsor.

How Do I Get Stakeholders to Endorse the Workplan?

The process of getting people to buy into the workplan is the endorsement process. Endorsement secures the commitment of stakeholders to actively support the workplan and work toward a successful project. Endorsement results in the commitment of project stakeholders to do whatever is required of them to make the project succeed as planned.

Communication with the customer, team members, and other stakeholders and their collaboration on the development of the workplan are essential to a successful workplan. Communication and collaboration are part of the endorsement process, and they set the stage for future endorsement of changes that occur during the project.

When Do I Update the Workplan?

A project workplan is a dynamic document that requires updating.

A project workplan is a dynamic document that requires updating whenever a significant change has occurred in the project scope, schedule, budget, team, or procedures. Updates may affect only one element of the workplan or many. You should review the workplan at least monthly, when preparing project progress reports and invoices, to ensure that changes are completed and communicated on a timely basis. Updating the workplan is the project manager's responsibility, but each member of the team should be alert for circumstances that might dictate workplan revision. Remember that, if a workplan is updated, the updated portions require endorsement just as the original version did. It is helpful to indicate the date and revision number on each page of the appended information, for example, in a footer. In this way, workplan recipients will not confuse updated material with original material.

What Are the Elements of a Workplan?

Certainly, one of the most commonly asked questions is: "What information should be included in the workplan?" Obviously, the contents of a workplan will vary from project to project. Large, complex projects, high-risk projects, and strategic projects will all require more planning and more extensive workplans than simple, straightforward projects. However, although workplan contents will vary, common elements should be found in all workplans.

Most of the remainder of this monograph presents the essential elements of the workplan, the information that should appear in all workplans, and the additional elements that are included in workplans on a project-specific basis (see page 129).

Essential Workplan Elements

The essential project workplan elements include:

- Definition
  - Objective
  - Scope
  - Work breakdown structure

- Resources

- Schedule

- Budget

- Instructions
  - Customer information and involvement
  - Procedures
  - Control
  - Progress measures
  - Records management
  - Financial management
  - Billing
  - Risk management

- Quality management plan

- Customer service plan

- Change management plan

- Closure plan

What Needs To Be Done? The Definition

The project definition is a statement of what will be done. It should reflect the project manager's understanding of the project and be based on a strong commitment to the customer. The definition can include material from a variety of sources, including the customer's scope, the request for proposals, the proposal to the customer, records of negotiation, and the contract with the customer. Care should be taken to review each of these documents and to ensure that the project definition is consistent with each of these documents.

The project definition section of the workplan typically consists of the project objective and scope and the work breakdown structure, which describes the tasks associated with the project and the deliverables that will result from the work.

Objective

The project objective describes the result to be achieved when the project is complete. The objective should be linked to the project vision, convey the big picture to the project team, and help the team stay focused on the desired result. The statement should be succinct but must also be:

- Specific

- Uncomplicated

- Measurable

- Realistic and attainable, both technically and logistically

- Compatible with organizational policies and procedures

- Focused around the customer's vision, needs, and expectations

Scope

The contract scope is a description of the work that will need to be done to achieve the objective. The scope may define the work as a level of effort (for example, 1,000 labor hours) or as a result to be accomplished (for example, design a 10,000-sq. ft. warehouse) or as a combination of both. The project scope may consist of excerpts from the customer's scope statement or from the proposal, or it may be necessary to create a scope statement. In any event, the scope needs to be consistent with the contract and with the customer's expectations.

The project scope should define deliverables, which help form the basis for the work breakdown structure and the schedule. Deliverables typically include construction design documents or reports. However, on occasion, the deliverable is a service to the customer; for example, assisting the customer in facilitating a hearing or meeting or in providing program management services. The project team members need to know what the deliverables are and how they are described in the scope and contract.

The contract scope almost always is broad enough to allow considerable latitude of interpretation. Therefore, as a stand-alone statement, scopes almost never provide the level of detail necessary to control the work of the project team. Nevertheless, the scope is extremely important to the project manager, because it constitutes the legal statement of what has been agreed to and forms the basis for the work breakdown structure.

Work Breakdown Structure

Once the scope has been defined, the tasks and subtasks that will fulfill the objective of the project are defined. These tasks, commonly referred to as the work breakdown structure, are the foundation of project planning and control. A proper work breakdown structure is probably the most critical element in good scheduling and budgeting. Do not scrimp on the amount of time you spend developing the work breakdown structure. It is the foundation for everything you do.

For a small, short-duration project, the level of definition provided in the proposal may be detailed enough to prepare the work breakdown structure. However, on large projects, more detail on the tasks to be performed is essential.

After the project team is identified and individuals are assigned roles, the broad tasks have to be further defined in a work breakdown structure.

The work breakdown structure is a hierarchical list of tasks and subtasks to be performed during the life of the project. For a project activity to be recognized as a task (or subtask, sub-subtask, etc.), it must meet five criteria:

1. A definable beginning and end

2. A finite duration, with at least one start and one stop date

3. An associated level of effort

4. A state of completion that can be estimated at any time

5. A reviewable internal or external deliverable at the task's completion

If an item does not meet all of these criteria, it should not be included in the work breakdown structure.

Tasks are further divided into subtasks and sub-subtasks whenever the project manager expects to control work below the task level or desires management information — for example, cost and progress — at a more detailed level. The need to define the relationship between tasks and their subparts is the reason the work breakdown structure must be hierarchically organized. Because the work breakdown structure is hierarchically organized, one of the best ways to create it is to use an outlining procedure or tree-diagramming technique. Outlines conveniently indicate the relationship between tasks and subtasks in a way that we all understand. Word processing software, such as Microsoft Word, as well as most project management programs, provide outlining templates, which allow relationships between a task and its subtasks to be shown. Most programs will accept up to seven levels of subordination.

Tasks are either in scope or out of scope, but not both. Be sure your project definition addresses all in-scope tasks. If a scope is vague, seek clarification. Vague scopes often lead to inappropriate work breakdown structures and ultimately to unfulfilled expectations on the part of the project stakeholders.

At this point, it is worth distinguishing between a milestone and a task, because they are often confused. A milestone is an important, time-precise project event. Milestones usually denote when certain tasks must be completed if the project is to remain on schedule, but the milestone itself is not a task because it does not meet all the criteria of a task. Although milestones are not tasks, they may be included in the work breakdown structure as a reminder of the task completion schedule.

Sometimes items that are neither tasks nor milestones are found in the project objectives statement; for example, keep the customer happy. It will require effort to keep the customer happy, it can be inferred that the duration is for the length of the contract, its success is measurable, but it does not have a defined scope of work. Therefore, although keeping the customer happy is important, it is not a task.

When project subparts are grouped together to form a higher level task or subtask, the higher level is referred to as a task or subtask roll-up. These roll-up tasks are the sum of their parts, and it follows that the cost of a roll-up task is also the sum of the costs of the parts. On the other hand, the duration of the roll-up may be less than the sum of the parts' duration, if some or all of the parts may be accomplished simultaneously rather than sequentially.

Roll-ups are useful, particularly when project management software programs are used, because they facilitate overall project monitoring, giving the project manager a comprehensive picture of project status.

If project managers take the time to develop work breakdown structures that hierarchically reveal the relationships between major tasks and minor tasks and use the appropriate project management software, projects will be more efficiently monitored and controlled and potential problems more readily identified. Project management software can generate reports that show detail ranging from the lowest level of subtasks in the hierarchy to the highest level of rolled-up tasks to anything in between. Project managers can view project information at all levels and can disseminate to team leaders and other stakeholders the task information relevant only to them.

The work breakdown structure is the key to efficient project management.

The work breakdown structure is the key to efficient project management because a number of remaining vital elements of the workplan rely on it, including the project resources, schedule, and budget. These workplan elements cannot be completed without the foundation provided by the work breakdown structure.

For a specific example of the steps involved in defining work tasks, see Defining Work Tasks: A Case Study, on page 138.

Who Is Going To Do The Work? The Resources

The project resources section of the workplan defines the personnel for the project team and nonpersonnel resources. Any positions to be assigned or equipment and services to be provided should be listed here so that associated costs can be included in the budget and schedules can be developed. Include anything not available through usual channels without prior scheduling or that must be purchased or leased specifically for and charged directly to the project. (For major programmatic projects, the nonpersonnel resources might include office space, furniture, and fixtures.)

Usually, everybody who will contribute effort to the project is not listed by name; however, all key team members should be listed (the project sponsor, senior reviewer, lead engineer, engineers, task managers, and key support staff leads), and the balance of the team should be designated by role (structural engineer, technician, graphic artist). Even if you do not know who will be assigned for certain tasks, be sure to keep a placeholder in the team roster for everyone you might need. Later, when you create your schedule and budget, you will be glad you did.

A project organization chart is a good way to begin listing human resource needs. The total number of people needed to complete a project will always depend on the schedule: If a longer time for completion is available, a fewer number of full-time workers will be required. Obviously then, the final estimate of project resources must be made in conjunction with the development of the schedule.

When Is the Work Going To Be Done? The Schedule

The schedule defines the order in which tasks will be accomplished, the specific time frame allocated to each task, and the start and finish dates of each task. All levels of the work breakdown structure need not be indicated on the schedule. A good schedule is only as detailed as necessary to measure progress and to efficiently use project staff and other resources.

Schedules may be resource driven; that is, controlled by the availability of resources. They may also be driven by required project finish dates, which may be the result of customer desires, regulatory requirements, or other needs.

Two things should be kept in mind about schedules. First, schedules change. A good project manager anticipates change and builds in extra time, or float time, to help accommodate the change. Remember, the customer must always approve any schedule changes. Second, schedules must be realistic. The customer will have a specific completion date in mind, which may be incorporated into the contract. If the customer's desired completion date cannot be met, or if any schedule contained in the proposal is unrealistic and cannot be met, a project manager should seek assistance in either acquiring added resources (internal or external) or working with the customer to develop a mutually agreeable, realistic schedule. Under no circumstances should a project manager promulgate a project schedule that he or she knows cannot be met.

Under no circumstances should a project manager promulgate a project schedule that he or she knows cannot be met.

Schedules may be created in many forms, with the most common being the Gantt chart. Numerous project management software packages provide scheduling capabilities. The choice of whether to use specialized computer scheduling software should always be made on the basis of selecting the simplest technique that will serve the project's needs. For simple projects, even handwritten schedules may suffice.

How Much Is the Work Going To Cost? The Budget

Financial management of the project begins with the budget. Budgets are dependent on the scope, the work breakdown structure, project resources, and the schedule. The budget constitutes the project manager's best estimate of the cost of completing the project work. The project manager should be willing to have his or her performance measured against, among other things, how well budgets are met.

A project budget must be realistic. Budgets should never be set lower than expected costs and should include an appropriate contingency allowance for unexpected changes other than customer-approved scope changes, which should be customer funded. Budget contingencies should be based on the expected accuracy of the estimates. Contingency allowances of 10 to 15 percent are common even when quite accurate estimates are available for use in setting budgets.

Remember that a distinction between what the customer has agreed to pay (contractual price) and the project budget may exist. But a project manager cannot be expected to deliver miracles. If after repeated attempts at developing a budget, the budget exceeds the contractual price, the project manager should determine what can be accomplished within the contractual price and seek to modify the scope, the work breakdown structure, the schedule, or a combination of these. This often will require assistance from others who will be expected to endorse the plan. A cardinal rule in budgeting is that whenever the scope, schedule, or assigned project resources change, a corresponding budget change is mandatory.

Budgets should always include all project activities that will be directly or indirectly charged against the project. All too often, project budgets do not include allowances for major project elements, such as project planning, quality assurance and control, and project closeout. Every work activity (task, subtask, etc.) requiring an expenditure of resources should be included in the budget.

Budgets should also be spread over tasks, rather than being considered as a lump sum. Unless a project workplan contains a planned rate of expenditure by task, it is very difficult to determine if a task is on budget or schedule. The rate at which resources are planned to be expended (hence the rate at which cost is accrued) is often called the burn rate. Burn rates, both planned and actual, are often expressed in graphical form as the plot of planned or actual cost versus time since project inception. The resulting graphical display of cumulative costs, labor hours, or other performance measures plotted against time are often referred to as S curves. The name derives from the S-shape of the curve, which is usually flat at the beginning and end and steep in the middle. This curve depicts a normal project's cost over time, where the burn rate is slow and deliberate at the beginning of a project, accelerated during project execution, and then slow again at the end of a project.

Budgets require updating whenever scope changes occur, and updates must occur prior to the time that additional work begins. Failure to obtain agreement from all project stakeholders regarding changes to the budget prior to undertaking additional work often leads to misunderstandings, customer discontent, and poor project performance.

How Is the Work Going To Be Accomplished? The Instructions

Project instructions include a myriad of information ranging from assignment of responsibility and authority to execution methodology. Typically, instructions will address customer information and involvement, procedures, control, progress measurement, records management, and billing. At a minimum, instructions should contain a listing of any procedure unique to the project and should outline the methods by which the work of the project team will be directed, measured, and managed by the project management. Unlike some of the other workplan categories, this area of planning tends to continue throughout the project: as work on some deliverables is completed and new work begins, the new work may require additional instructions.

Customer Information and Involvement

This section should briefly summarize pertinent information about the customer and the customer's staff who will be involved in the direction of the project. The degree and type of customer involvement should be described and the desired communication links should be included. This section is also a good place to indicate the schedule and scope for customer review meetings.

Procedures

This part of the project workplan should mention any unusual procedures that the project team will be expected to follow. These may be customer-specific or project-specific. Examples include procedures for public involvement, press releases, and customer communication. If no special procedures are involved, this section will simply state so. Otherwise, this section should note any out-of-the-ordinary methods that will be employed.

Control

If the project manager is going to truly manage something, he or she must be able to affect the outcome of various circumstances by exercising control. In controlling the outcome of a project, you will be controlling the actions and attitudes of your fellow team members. Experience has shown that teamwork and morale are enhanced when those whose actions will be controlled understand the means by which control will be exercised.

This section should outline the project manager's expectations and methods by which control will be exercised. For example, the project manager may designate certain team members as being responsible for certain tasks. The project manager would direct the activities of the task leaders who, in turn, would direct those team members assigned to the specific task(s). Other potential items for this section include a description of what reports are needed and their contents as well as descriptions and schedules for team meetings.

Progress Measures

Progress measures provide cost and budget information upon which project management decisions are founded. Most often the appropriate measures are those that compare current project-to-date information against planned schedule and budget. These measures should be used in the context of both actual and budgeted expenditures of time and money. Always remember that "budgeted" refers to what you planned to spend in terms of time and money and "actual" refers to what really happened. Following are some commonly used project progress measures:

- Actual Cost of Work Performed (ACWP)

- Budget at Completion (BAC)

- Budgeted Cost of Work Performed (BCWP)

- Budgeted Cost of Work Scheduled (BCWS)

- Cost Variance is BCWP - ACWP (CV)

- Cost Performance Index (CPI) (equal to BCWP/ACWP)

- Estimated Cost at Completion (EAC)

- Earned Value (equal to percent complete x BAC)

- Schedule Performance Index (SPI) (equal to BCWP/BCWS)

- Percent Complete (equal to BCWP/BAC)

Never attempt to calculate percent complete as being equal to percent of budget spent. This is probably the single most common mistake in measuring progress.

Records Management

Projects tend to create a great variety and volume of records. Many of these records need to be archived after the project is completed to provide a documented record of, among other things, design assumptions, the decision-making process, and performance information. In addition, these records are extensively used during project execution. Project instructions should define which records should be saved and how records should be managed. The project closure plan, which is discussed later in this monograph and in detail in the monograph *Close Project*, should identify which records will be archived.

Project records should be organized for quick access.

Project records should be organized for quick access. For many projects, a series of tabbed, three-ring binders will suffice, but more sophisticated techniques may also be required, particularly for management of electronic files. Occasionally, customers will have specific requirements for record keeping and may require that their own systems be used. In any event, records should be organized in categories that make information easy to store and find. Within categories, information should usually be kept in chronological order. Where possible, differentiation should be made between records that are intended to be permanent and those that will be discarded after project closeout.

Remember that all records are not necessarily generated on paper. Increasingly, computations, text, and even drawings are generated electronically. Do not forget to archive hard copies of such documents, as needed. The records management section of the workplan should describe how and where records are to be kept, who is responsible for which records, and who has the authority to purge project files.

Financial Management

Financial management instructions that summarize the project's financial requirements should be prepared. This information helps the project manager oversee financial issues and helps the enterprise's management support the project manager with timely reviews of financial information. Information for these instructions comes from the contract, the negotiations, project setup forms, and an understanding of the customer's expectations. The type of information in the instructions includes the following:

- Contract financial issues, such as allowable charges, markups, and fee structures

- Income recognition issues, such as revenue recognition and control of nonbillable costs

- Responsibility for accounts receivable, including release of retainage

- Financial audit requirements of the customer

- Financial progress report requirements of the customer, including customer-approved formats

- Subcontractor payment guidelines and requirements

By consolidating the project's financial requirements into a set of instructions, the project manager, the customer, and the enterprise's management will be able to focus on the relevant financial information and clarify any misunderstandings in financial control before the project begins.

Billing

Billing instructions are a required part of the project setup activity and therefore must be included in the project instructions and reflect the terms of the contract. The contract usually provides guidance or specifies requirements for the following elements that are associated with billing:

- Billing format

- Payment terms

- Customer-requested backup

- Customer-approval process

- Customer payment cycle

These elements should all receive attention in the workplan so that billing procedures are clear. Clear billing instructions that meet the approval of the customer will ensure that the enterprise receives prompt payment of the invoices and that the enterprise and the customer can meet their own financial obligations.

Risk Management

It is said that what we worry most about almost never happens. It follows then that worrying about potential problems by identifying them in this section of the project instructions may be the best possible line of defense in preventing problems.

All projects entail at least a minor amount of risk; a few may even be fraught with high risk (see Common Risks next page). Accordingly, the complete workplan will contain a section that characterizes, as much as possible, potential risk and that outlines control measures for minimizing the negative effects of risk. Although it is difficult to generalize about risk, the wise project manager will try to anticipate what can go wrong and, knowing what can go wrong, will safeguard the project team as much as possible. Accordingly, the risk management section should include a brief discussion of what could go wrong as well as the anticipated reaction should Murphy's Law prevail. If nothing else, advanced risk planning will help the team be alert for problem signals, placing the team in a proactive, rather that reactive, mode.

Common Risks

Contractual

- New customer (e.g., no payment history)
- Contract type (e.g., design-build, joint ventures, etc.)
- Unfavorable liability/indemnification clauses
- 3rd party liability

Financial

- Method of compensation (lump sum, award fee, etc.)
- No agreement, or out-of-scope work
- Retainage
- Warranties/guarantees
- Loss or damage to electronic files
- Performance penalties
- Unclear scope on fixed price job
- Schedule delays
- Change in key staff or stakeholders
- Replacing a fired consultant
- Property transfer site assessments (PTSA)
- Close out requirements

Technical

- Project scope (high risk work)
- New technology (little or no proven track record of performance)
- Unrealistic schedule
- Change in key technical staff
- Technical errors
- Multiple office/firm delivery team
- Complex project

Compliance

- Safety (site conditions, fieldwork, construction, subcontractors, etc.)
- Environmental compliance
- Regulatory changes or code changes

How Will Quality Be Ensured? The Quality Management Plan

Every project must have a quality management plan, and that plan must outline the processes that will be embedded into the project to ensure that the customer's expectations of quality are met or exceeded. Quality projects do not just happen. They are the result of the project team being committed to producing quality work and the team management being committed to managing quality. Quality is enhanced when tasks are done right the first time. It is much more costly to correct mistakes at the time of final review than to eradicate them on a day-by-day basis.

In designing the quality management plan, the prudent project manager will use experience, either personal experience or the experience of other project managers, to anticipate possible problems and incorporate procedures into the plan to avoid these problems and past mistakes through quality assurance measures. The wise project manager will also know that quality does not mean perfection nor entail "gold plating." Quality means delivering to the customer what they want, on time and within budget.

The quality management plan should stress that each team member is responsible for producing quality work and for helping to ensure that their fellow team members do so as well. The plan should also identify senior consultants who will provide technical guidance on the work in their areas of expertise and review selected end-products throughout the project. Senior consultants should not produce any of the work they review to retain an unbiased, fresh perspective. The schedule, work breakdown structure, organization chart, and budget should reflect the senior consultants' participation in the project and any other quality control activities. A budget of 5 percent or more of production cost is common for quality control.

How Will the Customer Be Kept Satisfied? The Customer Service Plan

Good customer service is essential to customer satisfaction. Customer service is as real as technical product; therefore, a customer service plan can be developed to guide the actions of the team. The customer service plan and its components are described in the monograph *Build Customer Relationships*. The customer service plan can describe specific service products such as the turnaround time for providing meeting minutes and then describe the action and responsibility for delivering that service.

An informed customer is not necessarily a happy customer, but an uninformed customer is seldom satisfied.

As part of good customer service, good communication between the customer and the enterprise is essential. Whether customers undertake projects because they want to or because they are required to, they have a major interest in seeing projects come to fruition. Therefore, they have a real need to know what is going on so they can react to circumstances in a rational and timely fashion. An informed customer is not necessarily a happy customer, but an uninformed customer is seldom satisfied.

The planning requirements for communication vary depending on project size, customer wishes, customer staff, and other factors. At a minimum, planning for communication should identify progress meetings, written progress reports, and methods for dealing with changed conditions or project problems. Like all other tasks, this one should be appropriately scheduled and budgeted. If the project manager gives little attention to communication, he or she then communicates with the customer by exception — as the need arises and as problems develop.

As part of the customer service plan, briefly summarize pertinent information about the customer and the customer's staff who will be involved in the direction of the project. The degree and type of customer involvement should be described, and the desired communication links should be included. Also, indicate the schedule for and scope of customer review meetings. On large, complex, or strategic projects or when team members are located in several offices, the project manager may want to develop a separate communication plan (see page 130).

How Will Change Be Managed? The Change Management Plan

To the saying, "Nothing is more certain than death and taxes," we should add the word "change." You may be absolutely certain that at one or more times during a project, something will happen that you did not plan for. Such circumstances usually mean that the project will need to be modified. Since it is not possible to foresee all potential changes, a project manager should plan the methods by which change will be recognized and accommodated when it inevitably occurs.

You, as the project manager, are responsible for managing change. Change management means having a means to recognize that change has occurred and a process, endorsed by the customer and project team, for effectively minimizing any negative effects of the change in the project. A change management plan, which is part of the workplan, provides the framework for decision making when change occurs. The change management plan is described in detail in the monograph *Manage Change,* where the following five-step process, which is used to develop the plan, is described:

1. Identify the change.

2. Analyze the effects of change.

3. Develop a response strategy.

4. Communicate the strategy and gain endorsement for the change.

5. Revise the workplan and monitor performance.

The project manager can build the change management plan around these steps and then can make decisions regarding budgets, resources, and schedule.

How Will the Project Be Closed? The Closure Plan

The last responsibility of the project team is to close out the project.

There comes a time when a project is either completed or work ceases. The last responsibility of the project team is to close out the project. This means that all project stakeholders need to agree that the project is complete. At such time, project activities should end in an orderly fashion. Project closure will always involve final review of deliverables, submittal of final invoices, and archiving of permanent records. Closure may also entail feedback meetings with the customer or other stakeholders as well as postmortem activities among the project team members.

Traditionally, project closure has been an activity that occurs at the end of a project; however, successful project managers know that project closure must be a planned activity that occurs throughout the project, not just at the end.

Activities associated with workplanning can be separated into three stages that define the complete project closure process:

- Beginning the project — planning for closure

- During the project — ongoing closure activities

- Ending the project — final closure activities

Although it may seem unusual to plan for closeout during the workplan development, remember that the work breakdown structure describes when to close tasks and when to close the project. One of the five criteria that define a task is that the task must have a stop date. Knowing the stop date of the tasks, as well as the overall schedule for the deliverables, is a major step in describing the closure procedures.

The project closure plan, which is described in detail in the monograph *Close Project*, should specify the closeout process and the records to be archived. Remember, legal requirements and enterprise requirements must be met in archiving.

Additional Workplan Elements

A number of additional workplan elements are sometimes needed to complete a workplan. These elements are not necessary for every workplan. Instead, they are used only if warranted by the specific circumstances of the project. The following are the most common additional workplan elements:

- Communication plan

- Health and safety plan

- Subcontract plan

- Risk management plan

- Contingency plan

- Database management plan

- Sampling and analysis plan

- Regulatory interface plan

- Graphics plan

- Document production plan

- Special accounting features plan

- Reward and recognition plan

Communication Plan

Normally included only when requested by the customer or on large, complex, or strategic projects or when team members are located in several offices, the communication plan is a description of how verbal and written communications among project stakeholders will occur. It delineates how communication is to be routed and who will receive what information. (See *How Will the Customer Be Kept Satisfied? The Customer Service Plan*, page 126.)

Health and Safety Plan

The health and safety plan is used whenever the project may entail work for which special health or safety precautions are needed. Examples would include any project involving hazardous materials or entry into confined spaces. The plan should list specific training needed by team members, procedures to be followed, and any other information relating to the adherence of approved health and safety regulations.

Subcontract Plan

The subcontract plan describes the work to be done by subcontractors and, whenever possible, identifies them specifically. If the project is required to use minority-owned businesses, woman-owned businesses, or other specified classes of subcontractors, the required entities and their extent of participation will be shown. In some cases, a project team may include, by agreement, subcontractors for which specific types or amounts of work have been specified. Such agreed-upon targets should be described in the subcontract plan.

Risk Management Plan

A risk management plan includes the steps associated with identifying, quantifying, and responding to project-specific risks. It includes maximizing the results of positive events and minimizing the consequences of adverse events. The development of responses to risk involves strategies for avoidance, mitigation, and acceptance of various risk elements as determined on a case-by-case basis.

Contingency Plan

If some future event may stop, delay, or materially change a project, the workplan may include a contingency plan describing what actions will be taken by the project team. Every project needs to include some degree of contingency planning. Usually it will suffice to cover possible changes in the change management and risk management plans and the budget; however, project managers who anticipate major changes in a project may elect to include a contingency plan.

Database Management Plan

A database management plan is required whenever software that is not a enterprise-wide standard will be used on the project. The use of nonstandard software may be customer dictated or necessary because of project complexity. Additionally, many geographic information systems, computer-aided engineering, and other automation tools use relational databases, which require careful management. The database management plan is essential to maintain data integrity and to facilitate orderly electronic transmission of data among project stakeholders. The plan should specify who has responsibility to create, retrieve, update, and delete data files.

Sampling and Analysis Plan

If a project requires a significant amount of work obtaining and analyzing samples, a sampling and analysis plan will be included. The plan should specify sampling techniques, locations, responsible team members, chain-of-custody protocols, analysis procedures, and any other information regarding sampling and analysis activities.

Regulatory Interface Plan

A section on regulatory interface should also be included in the workplan whenever specific protocols for interacting with regulatory agencies exist. This section will identify the protocols, describe the agencies affected, and indicate responsible team members.

Graphics Plan

Graphics plans are becoming more common as the use of graphic software increases. They are valuable elements of the workplan if special or customer-dictated graphics software is to be used. The graphics plan is also valuable if multiple offices are involved. Graphic standards are appropriate for most projects and should be used unless the customer expressly requests otherwise. These standards can be incorporated into the workplan by reference. Some managers like to include copies of the cover sheets of such references. This practice helps call attention to their use and provides a reference to the complete standard.

Document Production Plan

Document production plans should be developed for projects that have document production needs that deviate from our standard. These deviations could be driven by the customer's requirements or by the complexities of the document or its production. For example, when a customer requires that their document standards be applied to the project's documentation, a description of their standards should be included or referenced in the project workplan. Another example of a project that might require a document production plan would be a large report produced in different offices. In this case, the production plan helps ensure consistency.

Special Accounting Features Plan

If any nonstandard accounting procedures are to be used, they should be specified in a section of the workplan called special accounting features plan. Special accounting features may be requested by the customer or may be needed when a consulting enterprise is acting as a subcontractor or joint venture partner on a project.

Reward and Recognition Plan

A reward and recognition plan is very useful in maintaining team morale and productivity. The plan should delineate procedures that will be used in order to recognize project-related achievement. Reward and recognition can also be part of the closure plan. (See the monograph *Close Project*.)

The Workplan and the Project Delivery Process

Of the five elements of the project delivery process — chartering the team, developing the workplan, endorsing the project, managing change, and closing the project — developing the workplan is the key essential element, because it sets the other processes in motion: the endorsement process cannot occur unless the workplan is complete; the change management process cannot occur with a reasonable chance of success unless the workplan provides the baseline information; the closure plan requires the definition of tasks provided by the work breakdown structure in the workplan; and although team chartering should occur before the workplan is complete, developing the team into a high-performance team cannot occur without a complete workplan. Therefore, as the project manager and leader of the workplan effort, you should pay particular attention to how the workplan will relate to the other essential elements of the project delivery process. Each of these elements is discussed briefly below and in more detail in separate monographs.

Chartering the Project Team

Team chartering is the act of guiding a team through the process of defining itself: its scope, its goals, its behaviors, and all the other elements that are essential for a team if it is to have clarity of purpose and direction, which is essential for high performance. Chartering the project team is one of the first activities to begin after the notice to proceed on project work has been received. The results of team chartering naturally lead into project workplanning. In fact, the people identified in the team chartering process are the individuals who will create the project workplan under the leadership of the project manager.

Endorsement

Effective endorsement results in projects where the team, management, customers, and essential third parties all focus on the same project objectives; support the team efforts to accomplish those objectives as described in the project workplan; and commit to offer whatever assistance is needed to successfully complete the project.

Project Team

Endorsement is the unifying factor that transforms a collection of individuals into a team. Project team endorsement occurs when those expected to do the work described in the project workplan participate in the planning, understand what is expected of them, and commit to completing the project as planned. Without team endorsement, there can be no real teamwork.

Enterprise Management

Endorsement by management occurs when those controlling the corporate resources formally apply their experience to improving the project workplan and officially commit to supplying the resources necessary to execute the workplan.

Customer

Customer endorsement is the opportunity to involve the customer in reviewing, understanding, and agreeing to the details of the workplan. A workplan that deviates from what the customer needs and expects is a road map for confrontation, hard feelings, and mutual disrespect. Workplans must be shared with and endorsed by the customer. Remember, the customer is the owner of the project and has the principal stake in its success.

Third-Party Stakeholder

Third-party stakeholder endorsement is an optional task, necessary when third parties (permitting agencies, community officials, stockholders) must accept the final product before it can be judged complete and successful.

Managing Change

The process of managing change in a project represents one of the most important activities during the execution phase of the project. As a rule, when a project enters the execution phase, the project staff tend to focus on applying their area of technical skill to the deliverables. Although this focus on applying skills is essential, it must be combined with a focus toward managing change. If the project proceeds into the execution phase without a workplan that addresses change, the project will not be successful, largely because there is no logical way to measure and control change in the project.

Closing the Project

Project closure as a defined project delivery process element is important, yet it is frequently overlooked. Project closure is important because, if properly planned and implemented, it can lead to improved project performance as tasks are closed out and resources are demobilized in a timely manner. If closeout information is not properly disseminated and archived, project closure can be costly and frustrating for the customer, the project manager, and the enterprise.

The project closure plan, which is part of the workplan, provides the instructions for orderly project closure. The work breakdown structure of the workplan provides the basis for many of the closure activities, such as demobilizing staff, closing project numbers, and, most important, defining when a task is complete. Using the workplan as a basis for planning project closure also provides the opportunity to assign closure responsibilities to key staff of the project team.

Summary

The project workplan is an essential document, which the project manager uses to bring the project to a successful completion. However, to use the workplan effectively, it must be completed and endorsed before the project enters the execution phase. Workplans are required for all projects regardless of the project's perceived simplicity. Although the project may appear simple to the experienced project manager, preparing a workplan may uncover complexities that were initially overlooked. The workplan is also the most effective way for the project manager to communicate instructions and intent to the newly recruited project staff who may be unfamiliar with the project. The workplan provides the baseline for the project so that both progress and change can be measured and evaluated. Using a well-prepared workplan, the project manager can successfully lead the team through the project delivery process.

Other Resources

Bachner, John Philip. 1991. *Practice Management for Design Professionals: A Practical Guide to Avoiding Liability and Enhancing Profitability*. New York: John Wiley & Sons, Inc.

Brassard, Michael. 1989. *The Memory Jogger Plus*. Methuen, MA: GOAL/QPC.

Burstein, David and Frank Stasiowski. 1982. *Project Management for the Design Professional*. New York: Whitney Library of Design.

A Guide to the Project Management Body of Knowledge (PMBOK). 1996. Silva, NC: The Project Management Institute.

Hitt, William D. 1988. *The Leader-Manager*: *Guidelines for Action*. Columbus, OH: Battelle Press.

Defining Work Tasks: A Case Study

This case study illustrates the steps involved in the project definition stage of workplanning by means of an example. Our project is to partially complete construction of a wood-frame residence. The contract specifies that the project will be complete when the structure has been rough framed. From this information, we know that our project objective is to complete rough framing. We can assume that the contract does not specify a completion date but does define what is meant by completion of rough framing. At this point, we have in hand our project scope and objective. Our next activity is to determine what tasks must be accomplished to complete the project. To do so, we begin by making a list of all the tasks that will be required. At this time, we may not put the tasks in any order even though we will do so eventually. While we are creating our list of project tasks, we should also be preparing an initial estimate of how long each task will take.

Example Task List

A. Create project workplan   (1 day)

B. Supervise project   (throughout the project)

C. Erect rough framing	(6 days)
D. Pour concrete foundation	(1 day)
E. Stake out (survey)	(1 day)
F. Estimate materials	(1 day)
G. Order lumber	(1 day)
H. Order concrete	(1 day)
I. Excavate	(1 day)
J. Cure concrete	(5 days)
K. Strip forms	(1 day)
L. Complete exterior sheathing	(2 days)
M. Complete roof sheathing	(2 days)
N. Backfill foundation	(1 day)
O. Set forms	(1 day)
P. Place re-bar	(1 day)
Q. Order re-bar	(1 day)

Our next activity should be to determine how the tasks are related. For example, we know that the first thing that must be completed is to create the project workplan (A). All other tasks depend on completion of this task; therefore, no other task may begin until the workplan is completed. Another example is completing exterior sheathing (L) and roof sheathing (M). These two tasks are independent of one another; they can be done sequentially, with either being done first, or they can be done in parallel. However, exterior sheathing and roof sheathing are dependent on erecting the rough frame and neither of these two tasks can begin until the framing is complete. Erection of the rough frame is, in turn, dependent on several other tasks and so on.

In our example, we have listed 17 individual tasks. We may now wish to consolidate, or roll-up, some of the tasks. We may choose to roll-up the concrete operations under a single task called complete concrete foundation. Similarly, we might elect to roll-up all ordering functions under a task called order materials. If we did this, our work breakdown structure might look like this:

A. Create project workplan   (1 day)

B. Supervise project   (throughout the project)

C. Erect rough framing   (6 days)

D. Complete concrete foundation

    Place re-bar   (1 day)

    Set forms   (1 day)

    Pour concrete   (1 day)

    Cure concrete   (5 days)

	Strip forms	(1 day)
E.	Stake out (survey)	(1 day)
F.	Estimate materials	(1 day)
G.	Order materials	
	Lumber	(1 day)
	Concrete	(1 day)
	Re-bar	(1 day)
I.	Excavate	(1 day)
L.	Complete exterior sheathing	(2 days)
M.	Complete roof sheathing	(2 days)
N.	Backfill foundation	(1 day)

Our work breakdown structure is beginning to look a lot like an outline. This reinforces an earlier suggestion in this monograph: put your task list in outline form. Many word processing programs do this easily.

Our work breakdown structure still adds up to 29 days in duration; however, this does not necessarily mean that the project will require 29 working days since some tasks may be accomplished in parallel.

Our next activity should be to determine the hierarchical relationships among

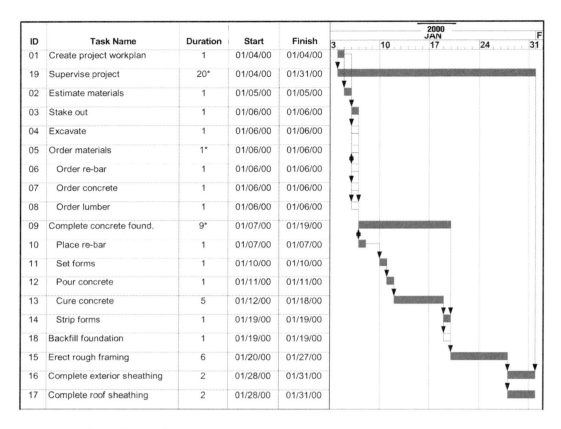

ID	Task Name	Duration	Start	Finish
01	Create project workplan	1	01/04/00	01/04/00
19	Supervise project	20*	01/04/00	01/31/00
02	Estimate materials	1	01/05/00	01/05/00
03	Stake out	1	01/06/00	01/06/00
04	Excavate	1	01/06/00	01/06/00
05	Order materials	1*	01/06/00	01/06/00
06	Order re-bar	1	01/06/00	01/06/00
07	Order concrete	1	01/06/00	01/06/00
08	Order lumber	1	01/06/00	01/06/00
09	Complete concrete found.	9*	01/07/00	01/19/00
10	Place re-bar	1	01/07/00	01/07/00
11	Set forms	1	01/10/00	01/10/00
12	Pour concrete	1	01/11/00	01/11/00
13	Cure concrete	5	01/12/00	01/18/00
14	Strip forms	1	01/19/00	01/19/00
18	Backfill foundation	1	01/19/00	01/19/00
15	Erect rough framing	6	01/20/00	01/27/00
16	Complete exterior sheathing	2	01/28/00	01/31/00
17	Complete roof sheathing	2	01/28/00	01/31/00

tasks and, from this information, determine the project duration. To do this, we should take advantage of one of the commercial software products.

When completed, our project work breakdown structure might look like the following figure. The example we have been working with is depicted in a Gantt chart. The Gantt chart is a common method of representing the hierarchical relationships that exist among project tasks as well as the schedule for their accomplishment.

In the work breakdown structure, notice that most of our tasks have task(s) that precede them, which indicates that the preceding task must be complete before the next task can begin. Notice also that a roll-up task's duration is dependent on the relationships of its subparts to one another. For example, in the order materials roll-up task (ID 5), all three subtasks can be done in parallel; therefore, the duration is the length of the longest subtask. But in the complete concrete foundation roll-up task (ID 9), the duration is the sum of the subtasks' duration, since each must be accomplished sequentially. For this example, our schedule is based on a 5-day work week. The software allows selection of various work cycles and automatically allows for nonworking periods such as weekends. Notice that our original outline called for a duration of 5 days for the concrete curing task (ID 13), but the Gantt chart diagram shows a duration of only 3 days. Since the task spans a weekend and since the concrete can cure during a nonworking period, the 2 weekend days plus the 3 working days provide the needed 5-day duration. Likewise, the total project duration, 18 days, is expressed in working days, not calendar days. On a calendar-day basis, this example spans from January 4 to January 27, a period of 24 days.

In a work breakdown structure, the hierarchical relationship between tasks may be any one of four possibilities. The most common is *finish to start*. That is, a task may not start until preceding tasks are finished. Other possibilities are *start to start*, *start to finish*, and *finish to finish*. In a start-to-start relationship, a task may start any time after its linked task starts; in a finish-to-finish relationship, the task may start any time but may not be finished until its partner task is finished. Finally, in a start-to-finish relationship, a task may not finish until its linked task has started. In the Gantt chart, these relationships are depicted by arrows that connect the linked tasks as shown in the figure on the following page.

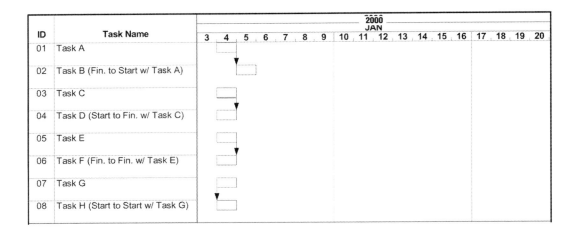

In our example Gantt chart (page 142), all of the illustrated tasks have finish-to-start relationships with their preceding tasks except the project supervision task (ID 19), which has a start-to-start relationship with the create project workplan task (ID 1) and a finish-to-finish relationship with the complete exterior sheathing task (ID 16).

Endorse Project

OVERVIEW

Endorsement is the final component in the planning phase of the project delivery process, which also includes chartering the team and developing the workplan. Once endorsement of the project workplan and charter is complete, the project moves into the execution phase.

Endorsement is not just the approval of the workplan as it has been thought of in the past. Rather, endorsement is the ongoing commitment on the part of the stakeholders to work toward a successful project as described in the charter and the project workplan. Endorsement should be substantiated in a document that is signed by all stakeholders for the project.

This monograph introduces the concept of endorsement and discusses the goals and benefits of endorsement, the endorsement process, the means for successful endorsement (informed involvement and collaboration), and the responsibilities of the stakeholders who should endorse the project.

Introduction

> *Always the surest guarantee of change and growth is the inclusion of living persons in every stage of an activity. Their lives, their experiences, and their continuing response–even their resistances–infuse with life any plan which, if living participants are excluded, lies on the drawing board and loses its reality.*
>
> *- Margaret Mead*

As Mead's quote suggests, the success of any project requires the inclusion of and a sensitivity to the people involved. This is certainly true in project management where, in recent years, techniques for encouraging meaningful participation have been formalized and successfully implemented. One of these techniques is endorsement, which is the process whereby the stakeholders buy into a project for its successful execution. Endorsement secures the stakeholders' commitments to actively support the project and work toward a successful project. Endorsement adopts a win-win strategy that is based on meeting the expectations of the customer and also satisfying the performance requirements of the enterprise.

Endorsement is part of the project planning process, which also includes chartering and developing the workplan. As part of the endorsement process, the charter and the workplan are carefully reviewed by the stakeholders, and their signatures are obtained to confirm the commitment. However, endorsement is not just a single event, such as approving a workplan; it is an ongoing process. Endorsement occurs during project planning and recurs whenever buy-in is needed to accommodate change during project execution.

True and successful project endorsement differs from the traditional workplan approval because it results in commitment rather than a mere lack of objection. Where approval of a workplan usually means, I didn't find anything to reject, endorsement means "This is a good plan, and I commit myself to supporting it and ensuring a successful project."

Project endorsement is a new process that has not been part of conventional project planning. As something new, endorsement requires effort beyond that normally associated with project planning. However, endorsement is worth the effort because it substantially improves project success as viewed by many different stakeholders. In fact, where endorsement has been practiced, project managers report that the process has succeeded in identifying and avoiding pitfalls in the original workplan and charter and has succeeded in securing senior management's commitment.

Goal of Project Plan Endorsement

The goal of endorsement is to secure the commitment of customers and stakeholders, who are working from an informed knowledge base and have fully committed to successful project performance in accordance with the workplan and charter. To efficiently achieve the goal, the project manager should apply the following principles throughout the planning and endorsement phases of the project delivery process:

- Involve all critical stakeholders
- Orchestrate timely, informed involvement

- Emphasize collaboration

- Remain open to improvements and changes throughout the project

- Demand positive, active support

When project managers apply these principles, stakeholders (project team members, the enterprise's management, the customer, and essential third parties) can focus on the same project objective and support the team efforts. A good project endorsement procedure will:

- Foster mutual understanding of the project objective, the limitations toward meeting this objective, the need for resources to achieve the objective, and the overall direction the project staff will be pursuing toward achieving the project objective.

- Identify inherent risks associated with the project, and provide opportunities for all stakeholders to identify means to minimize the risks inherent in the project.

- Give all parties a stake in ensuring the success of the project by applying the endorsement process to initial planning and to changes that occur throughout the project.

- Result in commitment of staff, management, customer, and third-party stakeholders to do whatever is required of them to make the project succeed as planned.

Benefits of Project Endorsement

Project endorsement offers benefits to the project manager, the customer, the enterprise's management, and third-party stakeholders.

The project manager benefits from endorsement primarily because the process ensures that he or she will be in a position of leadership if the following requirements are met:

- All endorsees identify and suggest resolutions to any issues about which they are concerned.

- Senior management is actively committed to:

    - Providing the necessary staff when needed

    - Providing the required technology (skill base, knowledge, experience), tools, and resources (computers, office space)

    - Accepting the known risks

    - Advising and assisting in executing the project

- Project team members actively concur that the plan is workable, their staffing issues have been addressed, and they are committed to completing the project as described in the workplan.

- The customer reconfirms its commitment to the project and accepts the details of the workplan and charter, which may have been less understood at the proposal stage.

- Oversight and permitting agencies accept that the proposed project approach addresses their concerns and will meet their needs.

The customer gains the most from project endorsement, even when their involvement is indirect and passive, rather than face-to-face. Their greatest gain is that through endorsement all others working on the project have thought through the project execution phase, voiced their concerns, and jointly committed to project success. Through active involvement in project endorsement, the customer also gains:

- Assurances that their vision, needs, and expectations are clear

- Early, meaningful input into the specifics of the project approach and the detailed definition of the deliverables

- Early understanding of what to expect throughout the project so the customer can plan their use of the project products

- Better control of project service, and projects that meet expectations at a cost that reflects value to the customer

The Enterprise's management gains:

- An understanding of the project requirements, enabling evaluation based on the full range of criteria rather than on financial performance alone

- An understanding of the project resource needs, allowing the enterprise to commit to providing these resources

- An opportunity to improve project performance by timing resource demands to better fit with other priorities

- Early warning regarding known project risk factors and a consequent opportunity to assist in minimizing those risks

Through endorsement, third-party stakeholders gain the opportunity to influence the project before the planning is finalized. If involved at this early stage, they can contribute to the workplan and ensure that their concerns will be considered.

Elements of the Endorsement Process

The endorsement process has three elements: positioning for endorsement, signing the endorsement, and endorsing change. The process is used throughout the project whenever stakeholder commitment is needed to ensure success of the project.

Positioning for endorsement begins as soon as the relationship is established with the customer. The old sales adage that begins with, "tell them what you are going to tell them..." applies here. The project manager must begin early to describe the benefits of endorsement to the customer and to cultivate the customer's acceptance of endorsement as a process contributing to optimal project performance.

The second element in endorsement is the formal exercise of sign-off, conducted as a capstone to project planning. In every project, the customer and other key stakeholders should endorse the charter and the workplan. In addition, in projects where some form of partnership is being established between the customer and the enterprise, the partnership should also be endorsed, for example, in a charter document developed and signed prior to detailed definition of the workplan. Similarly, if the project has multiple phases, endorsement should be sought again as each new phase is defined and executed.

To bring closure to the planning process, the workplan is exposed to the scrutiny of others who must do their share to successfully execute the project.

To bring closure to the planning process, the workplan is exposed to the scrutiny of others who must do their share to successfully execute the project. When that scrutiny leads to true endorsement, the parties involved have fully accepted that the workplan can and will be carried out. In endorsing the project, all parties accept responsibility that extends beyond their narrowly defined role to fully support the efforts of the entire team toward making the project the success promised in the workplan. Once this has been achieved, the endorsement can be substantiated in a simple, one-page statement of endorsement that is signed by all stakeholders and then reproduced and distributed to the signatories and other stakeholders. It is a good idea to frame a copy and hang it in the project office as a continual reminder of everyone's mutual commitment.

The third element in endorsement is endorsing change. As changes occur in the project, the project manager should secure the endorsement of those stakeholders who must commit to supporting the change. Following the five-step process for managing change, which is described in the monograph *Manage Change*, will generate the information that stakeholders need before they can confidently endorse a change.

On most projects, the project workplan must be aligned with the realities of what project staff, the enterprise's management, the customer, and other key stakeholders can confidently endorse. Few projects will be fully endorsable on the first pass, so original planning must be flexible enough to accommodate modifications that will lead to endorsement.

Two Approaches to Obtaining Endorsement

There are two basic approaches to obtaining endorsement. The first consists of joint development, review, and sign-off of the charter and workplan by the project team, the customer representatives, and the enterprise's management, including the project sponsor. This approach is used, for instance, when the project team and customer representatives have agreed to develop a partnership to manage the project. The second approach is to conduct independent presentations and sign-offs with each party, commencing with the project team (and key subcontractors), followed by the enterprise's management, and finally the customer and any other key stakeholders.

If stakeholders whose endorsement is being sought have been directly involved in the chartering process and the workplan development, then endorsement is relatively simple. As the stakeholders develop alignment around the vision, purpose, and definition of the project, this alignment is substantiated in a formal endorsement document. As the final step in the endorsement, all participants are asked to sign this document to verify their commitment to the project's success.

If the enterprise's management has not been directly involved in the team chartering and workplan development, the next step after the team has signed off is to provide the charter and workplan to management for review, discussion, and sign-off (see Presentation Tips, page 164).

Similarly, unless the customer has been directly involved in the development of the workplan or the charter (for example, in a partnering session), the documentation will need to be formally presented to the customer for discussion and sign-off. After sign-off, it can be presented to other key stakeholders, if desired.

If any of the above reviews cannot be conducted in a face-to-face meeting, the best arrangement is to send a written copy of the documentation to the appropriate party, give them time to read it, and then hold a telephone conference to review it and obtain agreement for the endorsement.

Troubleshooting: What If the Customer Will Not Endorse the Project?

The primary value of the endorsement process is as a means of building mutual trust and commitment to the project. Even understanding its intent, some customers are unable or unwilling to participate in this process, perhaps preferring to maintain a traditional, arms-length relationship. Sometimes it helps to have the project sponsor, or another senior-level person communicate directly with senior-level staff in the customer's organization. If this is unsuccessful, the project manager should aim for the highest level of agreement that can be attained at the start of the project, get this in writing, and then keep working toward a higher level commitment at subsequent reviews during the project execution.

The primary value of the endorsement process is as a means of building mutual trust and commitment to the project.

Two Techniques for Improving the Endorsement Process

Although there are no firm rules about how endorsement is best accomplished, two techniques are generally used to facilitate the process: informed involvement and collaboration.

Informed Involvement

For the stakeholders to provide meaningful endorsement, they must be fully informed of the project. Early in the project, however, it is often difficult to define all aspects of the project in enough detail to meet the needs of all stakeholders. The key is to identify the information needs of the stakeholders, get that information to them as soon as possible, and clearly define how additional information will be developed and transmitted throughout the project. Frequent communication will help to reduce the likelihood of stakeholders not endorsing the project. Numerous strategies can be used to get the information to the stakeholders in sufficient but not overwhelming detail and in a timely manner. Some of these strategies are listed below.

Frequent communication will help to reduce the likelihood of stakeholders not endorsing the project.

Focused Transmittals

Too often project workplans are all-inclusive documents that overwhelm rather than inform the reader. The workplan can be much more informative if it is transmitted with instructions that clearly focus readers on the portions of most relevance to them. For example, the CAD technician can be directed to the graphics plan, while the enterprise's management representative may be directed to the risk management sections. A good table of contents will allow the endorsement participants to quickly identify and scan other parts of the project workplan that affect their endorsement. In some cases, only part of the project workplan needs to be transmitted to and reviewed and endorsed by specific stakeholders. Keep in mind, however, that stakeholders may later reject any part of the workplan or charter that they have not had the opportunity to endorse.

Edited Documentation

Project managers know their subject, their project approach, and their management tools so well that they often write project workplans that are clear only to themselves. Having the project charter, workplan, and endorsement clarified by an editor can greatly improve the documents' abilities to communicate effectively. Examples of misunderstandings caused by lack of clarity abound, and project managers must be aware that most stakeholders will interpret the document in a way that best meets their needs, then be offended if that interpretation is rejected later. Clarity is essential.

Phased Endorsement

In the all too common case where all issues cannot be resolved in the project endorsement phase, the project workplan must acknowledge the issue and clearly specify when in the project execution phase the issue will be more fully addressed and brought forward for the stakeholder endorsement. This step is most important for those stakeholders who have traditionally felt left out of the process. Instead of saying, "We can't answer your question now," the endorsable project workplan says, "We understand the question, plan to study it, and will answer it in Task X with a summary provided for review and comment by MM/DD/YY." This type of phasing is particularly common when there are questions regarding which technical methods are to be applied. Instead of making an uninformed, rash selection of a technical approach to meet the needs of the planning phase, the project manager should identify those decisions that need to be made and include statements in the workplan that reflect this, such as, "We will investigate the options and make a selection based on the findings."

Other strategies for effective information dissemination are available through discussion with more experienced project managers.

Collaboration

Project execution is an effort where all stakeholders must work as a team to accomplish their part in the project. In today's workplace, such teamwork is better achieved through collaboration than through a command-and-control approach. Project endorsement recognizes the need to involve all parties, from customer representatives through project technicians. Successful teamwork involving this broadened concept of the project team is engendered through collaboration; that is, through working together toward a common objective.

The bottom line is to develop the workplan, and indeed the entire project, in a manner that clearly allows the stakeholders to collaborate and contribute to improved project success.

Identify Constraints

One technique to encourage collaboration is to identify constraints (limitations that cannot be ignored or overcome) and to optimize or prioritize resources based on those limitations (time, budget, skills, etc.). This technique can be extremely useful in articulating the common objectives in terms that all parties can understand and accept. Articulating mutually acceptable objectives may not be easy, but it is necessary. Obtaining agreement on mutually acceptable objectives may require thoughtful discussions, but the effort will lead to collaboration in other areas and will be rewarded by enhanced teamwork and overall project support.

For example, if the stated objective is to minimize costs–that is, the objective is to complete the design with the lowest possible expenditure of labor–then management may be satisfied, but the project team may see cost conflicting with doing a quality job. All parties may be better satisfied if the objective is stated in terms of constraints and optimized resources. For a fixed price contract, the statement may be, "The objective is to efficiently complete the design to technical specifications within the time constraints (two months) and labor constraints (1,000 labor hours)." Given that objective, the customer can assist in optimizing the resources, and the staff can apply their skills to defining the means of completing the design within the specified constraints of time and labor hours. This approach of defining objectives in terms of constraints and optimized resources leads to creative technical solutions, rather than conflict-ridden project budget overruns.

If conflict arises, avoid stating the objective at a higher level of abstraction. While you might initially gain agreement, the issue will resurface later, typically at a critical time. Disagreements should first be approached with a real desire for understanding. Then seek a result that is aligned with the project vision and that is based on what is right rather than who is right.

Develop an Open Process

Another technique to encourage collaboration is to develop an open process and project environment. An atmosphere of collaboration can develop only if the stakeholders perceive that the decision makers (project management) are truly open to suggestions for improvement. Most project managers consider themselves open to constructive suggestions, but few successfully convey this openness to all members of the project team. And perception is what counts. If project management is not perceived as open to improvements, then good suggestions will be grumbled about at the staff level and never brought forward for the betterment of the project. If project management is perceived as open and the decision-making process is well defined, the team will be constantly improving the project and continually making it a better effort than management could envision alone.

Following are some of the signs of an open process and environment and some of the signs of a closed process and environment:

Indicators of Open Process and Environment

- Listening more than talking

- Encouraging flexibility (minimal arguing from fixed positions)

- Defining objectives and requesting suggestions for methods to achieve them

- Improving on approach based on staff suggestions

- Decision making through collective discussion and agreement

Indicators of Closed Process and Environment

- Defending positions and decisions (justify why changes cannot be made)

- Explaining why it is the way it is rather than comparing the pros and cons of alternatives

- Completely defining methodologies without input

- Grumbling by staff off-line

- Discouraging suggestions during meetings

Project managers and the project planning activities they oversee should encourage openness. If signs of closed processes exist during the endorsement phase, the project is unlikely to achieve success in the eyes of all stakeholders. Openness to improvements should be maintained throughout the project.

Critical Stakeholders

All completed projects, regardless of size and breadth, must satisfy the customer, the project manager, the project staff, and the enterprise's management. Many completed projects must also satisfy other stakeholders, such as permitting agencies, affected neighbors, public groups with a vested interest (stockholders or taxpayers), and environmental reviewers. Recognizing these stakeholders early in project planning allows development of a charter and workplan that address their interests and concerns and circumvents potential pitfalls. In particular, any stakeholder who has endorsed the project becomes an advocate for the project. Conversely, any stakeholder excluded from the endorsement phase becomes a potential critic whose arguments will not have been addressed. The consequence of unsatisfied criticism is project rejection, or at least delay, until the objections can be resolved.

Following is a brief description of the project stakeholders — including the project team, the customer, the enterprise's management, and third-party stakeholders — and their responsibilities.

The Project Team

Project team endorsement occurs when those expected to do the work described in the project workplan and charter carefully review what is expected of them and commit to completing the project as planned. If there are problems with the workplan or charter, each team member has responsibility for helping the project manager modify these documents so they can be fully endorsed.

Project team members who must endorse the project would be those task leaders, technical leads, reviewers, and staff whose contribution to the project will significantly affect its successful outcome. The project manager must ensure that those members who are outside of the office, or in other subconsulting enterprises, participate in the endorsement process.

The Customer

Project managers should provide every opportunity for the customer to participate in the endorsement process, including reviewing, understanding, and agreeing to the details of scope and methodology governing how their project will be accomplished. The customer has an opportunity to confirm, or modify and confirm, the workplan and charter, and at the same time to talk fully and frankly about project risks and uncertainties and preferred strategies for managing change.

Customer endorsement confirms that the customer is an equal partner with project staff and management in committing to the project. Customer endorsement is also a good time to review any opportunity for partnering that may have arisen since the proposal and contracting phases of the project. If new opportunities for partnering have arisen, the project manager should create a partnering plan, rework the project accordingly, and reconfirm the project endorsements received to date.

Enterprise's Management

The endorsement of the enterprise's management occurs when those controlling the corporate resources formally apply their experience to improving the project and officially commit to supplying the resources (personnel, computers, office space) necessary to execute the project. The endorsement of the management is an important part of the process because it signifies the commitment of the enterprise to actively provide the resources and support needed for project success.

The project manager must seek out those individuals who can deliver on the commitment.

The management representatives who will endorse the project will have to be identified as the charter and workplan are being developed. Most projects will be endorsed by a representative of the office in which the work will be performed who has the authority to deliver on the commitment to make the project a success. The project manager must seek out those individuals. In the case of complex or enterprise-wide strategic projects, endorsement may go to the highest levels of management. Where projects are being executed in more than one location, the endorsement of the management in all affected offices should be secured.

Third-Party Stakeholders

Third-party stakeholder endorsement is important when third parties (permitting agencies, community officials, stockholders, public action committees, or others) must accept the final project before it can be judged complete and successful. Providing key players an early opportunity to review and possibly contribute to the charter and workplan allows them to endorse the workplan and commit their efforts toward promoting its success.

Summary

Endorsement is the final component of the planning phase in the project delivery process. Endorsement means that stakeholders share a mutual understanding of the project and are committed to the project's success. In order for endorsement to be successful, the project manager must identify the key stakeholders, bring them into the endorsement process early in the project, and develop a collaborative project environment that encourages open communication among stakeholders.

Other Resources

Nierenberg, Gerard. 1986. *The Complete Negotiator.* New York: Nierenberg and Zeif.

Peppers, Don, and Martha Rogers. 1993. *The One to One Future.* New York: Doubleday.

Senge, Peter. 1990. *The Fifth Discipline.* New York: Doubleday.

Endorsement: Presentation Tips

The strategy for obtaining endorsement from persons who have not been directly involved in the project planning process includes several steps. The first step is to arrange to present the material to be endorsed (for example, charter or workplan) to the persons from whom you are seeking buy-in. The ideal format is a meeting, where you can provide a structured walk-through. The meeting should not last more than two hours. If a meeting is not possible, provide a written summary of the material and discuss it in a conference call. In either case — a face-to-face meeting or a phone call — use the following process:

Set the Context. Briefly explain your purpose in arranging for the presentation, what you would like to cover, and what action you are seeking. Make sure the participants understand the difference between endorsement and approval.

Affirm the Common Vision. Review the project vision, the project definition (objective, scope), and the team purpose. Gain agreement on the desired end result to encourage participants to work collaboratively toward this end.

Walk-through. Provide a brief step-by-step summary of the key points in the material you are covering and how these were developed. Include deliverables that are the result of the work breakdown structure and the approach being taken.

Describe the Benefits. You may want to briefly note any major advantages that can be gained via the approach you are taking, if these are not already apparent.

Discuss. After presenting the plan, seek feedback and answer any questions that remain. If there is disagreement on any area, you will need to employ negotiation techniques to develop a win-win solution. This solution will need to be reflected in the documents that are being endorsed.

Summarize. Encapsulate the key points resulting from the discussion in a concise document, not more than one to two pages in length, to be appended to the material being endorsed.

Commit. To complete the endorsement, obtain signatures of endorsees on a written commitment. If changes have been negotiated, document these in a memo of understanding and transmit this memo to the endorsees for their signature and return.

Distribute. Ensure that all parties who have endorsed the project receive final copies of the signed documents. The endorsement should also be shared with other key stakeholders in the project who were not part of the endorsement process, along with a cover memo clearly explaining its intent.

Manage Change

OVERVIEW

Change is an inevitable part of projects; therefore, change management is an essential part of project management. Planning for change by developing appropriate guidelines and processes is crucial to the successful execution of a project.

This monograph discusses the benefits of change management, the types and sources of change, and ways to manage change, including the development of a change management plan.

Introduction

A project is by definition an exercise in deliberate change or the planned application of technologies and resources to create a new state of understanding, capability, or physical condition; therefore, change and its management are an inevitable part of every project.

During project execution, deviations from the scope and contract will occur. The source of these deviations can be internal changes initiated by the project team; external changes initiated by the customer; or external changes that are a result of third-party stakeholders, availability of resources, changing construction and implementation costs, or other factors. The effect of these changes may be positive, providing opportunities to enhance value or save money, or they may be negative, threatening to increase project cost without adding value. Whether the effect is positive or negative, managing change during the execution phase of a project is an important factor in project success. For this reason, change management was selected to be an essential component of the project delivery process.

Managing change requires planning, discipline, and communication among team members and customer representatives. Projects do not fail because of change but because of a lack of recognition of change and of clear, consistent direction and leadership when confronted with the challenges of change.

This monograph presents the benefits of effective change management; the types and sources of project change; risk management, which is an important consideration in planning for change; the components of a basic change management plan; and the allocation of responsibilities for managing the plan.

Benefits of Effective Change Management

Effective change management occurs when early identification of the source of change and its effect on a project are realized. Next, a plan to manage change is developed, communicated to all parties, and implemented. If these steps have all taken place, the following is likely:

- Enhanced customer relationships

- Improved financial performance

- Reduced project delays

- Better project teamwork

- Improved management of project quality

Change management helps eliminate customer surprise.

Change management will enhance customer relationships. Because communication is continual and change is discussed expeditiously, the customer is not surprised.

Project budget and schedule performance can be improved and project delays can be minimized with effective change management. Too often a project budget overrun is due to inadequate change management. The cost and time to complete the work may increase because of a number of internal and external factors, including customer desires, innovations, and changes in the project team.

By practicing effective change management techniques, the cost and time required to implement the change are agreed to before the new work begins, ensuring buy-in from all parties.

Teamwork is enhanced and morale improved when potential conflict is resolved in a timely manner through negotiations. By identifying a change, determining its effect, developing an action plan, and communicating the plan to all parties, teamwork is strengthened.

Management of project quality is improved when the quality requirements of the project are related to the customer's expectations and are thoroughly described in the project workplan. These initial quality requirements are the basis for comparing the quality requirements that result from proposed changes. The project manager will need to resolve with the customer any differences between initial quality requirements and new quality requirements that are a result of change.

Types and Sources of Change

As previously mentioned, changes encountered during a project generally arise from within the project team, from the customer, or from an external source.

Changes arising from the project team may include the following:

- Scope creep — Scope elements increase in small increments until a significant change occurs.

- Increased level of effort — Unintended additions are made to the amount of work performed in execution of a task, usually occurring in relation to continual refinement or improvement of concepts or alternatives; for example, changes made to improve aesthetics or performance related to constructibility, reliability, or operability.

- Quality creep — A subtle change that occurs when individuals deviate from the quality standards developed for the project. Generally, quality creep occurs as individuals apply their personal preferences to the level of quality of a particular project element.

- New technologies and tools — The unfocused application of new technologies and tools, which leads to unfulfilled customer expectations and to project cost increases and schedule delays. This problem is generally associated with scope creep, increased level of effort, or quality creep.

- Personnel changes — Project team members may have to leave the team for a variety of reasons.

- Schedule improvements — Changes proposed to remove a threat to or to improve the chance of achieving milestones on time. These changes often involve the sequencing of tasks, or they may include design or process changes to enhance construction or implementation schedules.

Customer-initiated changes may include:

- Personnel changes — Customer representatives may also leave during a project.

- Scope creep — Customer-initiated, incremental increases in scope may also result in a significant change.

- Customer discretion — Customers may request a change or a change may occur because of customer action.

Changes originating from external sources, which may be manifested through either customer or team-initiated action, include:

- Mandated changes — Changes linked to third-party regulatory requirements, such as code revisions, regulatory changes, permit conditions, and discovered conditions.

- Availability changes — Changes in availability of materials, labor, equipment, and other resources.

- Construction or implementation cost changes — Design, process, or construction sequence changes needed to compensate for construction or implementation costs that were higher than estimated. These cost changes can include cost-savings opportunities.

A proactive, disciplined approach to change management is vital to the health of the project.

Whatever its origin, a specific change will often trigger additional changes from the customer and project team, resulting in various combinations of the types of change described above. Once this snowball effect begins, it becomes increasingly difficult to analyze or manage change. Therefore, a proactive, disciplined approach to change management is vital to the health of the project.

Setting the Context

Setting up projects for successful management of change begins with the contract, which should specifically address change. Although the contract can indicate the customer's expectations for how change will be managed, it is only a first step.

Another step that can be taken at the outset to promote effective change management is to discuss change and risk with the customer representative.

The project manager must learn about the customer's day-to-day operations and long-term expectations, including fiscal, regulatory, staffing, and community involvement expectations. This information will provide a better understanding of the context of the project and potential risks, changes, and opportunities.

The contract and scope form the baseline for the measurement of change and must be clear and complete so that change can be identified as it occurs. Creating quantifiable criteria to compare change with the scope is mandatory. These criteria are typically related to cost and time and can be used to compare the effect of change on the project. If developed at the beginning of the project and included in the workplan, these criteria can be used throughout the project as the basis for measuring the effect of change.

> **A** change management process will help maximize the results of positive change and minimize the consequences of negative change.

In managing change, as in other components of the project delivery process, early attention to the development of appropriate processes is a key to effective management. Management of change includes identifying, analyzing, planning for, communicating, and monitoring the uncertainties brought on by change. A change management process for the project, which is described in a change management plan, will help maximize the results of positive change and minimize the consequences of negative change.

Acknowledging Risk

A large part of change management is the acknowledgment that each project has certain risks or uncertainties associated with it that may affect the project in ways that cannot be specified in advance. The customer must provide guidance on identifying the risks and understand and accept the risks that are inherent in the project. These risks can arise from any source and, depending on how they are handled, may either threaten the project or support it. Risk often relates back to the nature of the contract, rather than the scope of the project. It may originate, for instance, as the result of a specific commitment or business decision made to satisfy customer expectations.

Although many situations can introduce risk into a project, part of analyzing risk is to determine the likelihood of a particular event occurring. A number of situations have been found to impose a higher likelihood of risk occurring, and project managers should be aware of these:

- A new customer with whom relationships have not been established
- A technically complex project
- An administratively complex project
- Difficulty in accessing needed resources
- A "hot" regulatory climate
- Exposure to liability

Considering these situations, a number of potential events should be seen as red flags:

- Customer is making an expensive decision, and the costs of research and testing are high.
- Customer has a severely limited budget or schedule for both design and construction.
- Customer has a costly problem imposed on it by external forces such as regulators.

- The solution with the lower initial cost has the higher life-cycle cost.

- An innovative, untested approach may be the best or least expensive solution.

The effect of the potential event on the project must be considered when developing the change management plan for the project. Also, the potential for risks to multiply should be examined. Even if risk is low, events that can have a critical effect on the viability of the project should be monitored carefully. Identifying risks and framing appropriate responses to them constitute a risk management plan, which, if applicable, should be a component of the change management plan or the workplan.

The Change Management Plan

During the project planning phase, a change management plan should be developed as a component of the project workplan. The change management plan describes the guidelines and processes the team will use to manage changes as they occur and leads to a thorough and orderly disposition of project changes. Following are descriptions of five elements that need to be addressed in a change management plan:

1. Identify the change.

2. Analyze the effects of change.

3. Develop a response strategy.

4. Communicate the strategy and gain endorsement for the change.

5. Revise the workplan and monitor the effects of change.

These five elements not only represent the contents of the plan, but they also represent the change management process.

1. Identify the Change

The change management plan must contain a process for identifying change issues, which are actions or circumstances that can cause a change in scope, personnel, cost, or schedule. The process should include routine assessments, such as scheduled project reviews, and should prescribe specific techniques that can be applied at any time.

The earlier the team can learn about a potential change, the sooner they can track it and plan for it.

Change issues may be identified by anyone. The project manager should encourage project team members to identify issues that could change the project workplan. Even if these issues are ultimately unfounded, it is better to have identified them and discounted them, than to have ignored them and had to address them later. The earlier the team can learn about a potential change, the sooner they can track it and plan for it. The change that causes the most damage is the one that is discovered when it is too late to do anything except to lament that the project team should have known.

The first step in assessing a potential change is to determine its type and source. Options and actions in response to change will depend on who proposes or identifies the change as well as the type of change, whom the change affects, and whether the effect is positive or negative. Designating financial responsibility for the change will also depend on this assessment.

The change management plan should also provide a change issues record: a template for recording change, which will become a part of the project documentation. In practice, the project manager should concisely indicate the type and source of the change issue, as well as any other appropriate information.

2. Analyze the Effects of Change

Verifying the change issue is the responsibility of the project manager or a team member familiar with the workplan, particularly with the scope, the schedule, and the budget. The project manager verifies the change issue by determining whether it leads to a change in scope, cost, or schedule. For this reason, the change management plan must describe methods that will be used to analyze various types of change. The analysis is facilitated when the elements of the workplan have been entered into the project planning software, because the potential effects of a change on various aspects of the project can be predicted. For example, any change to scope, whether it is additive, deductive, or qualitative, will affect the cost, therefore budgets must be adjusted to reflect the change. Based on the analysis, the project manager should be prepared to explain the effect and the value of the change to the customer.

Any change to the scope will affect the cost.

3. Develop a Response Strategy

Once the type and source of change have been identified and their effects on the project have been analyzed, the next step is to develop a specific response strategy. The change management plan should provide guidance on the general alternatives and parameters. Here are some key questions that can be used to build the response:

- What needs to be done?
- Who is going to do it?
- When is it going to be done?
- How much will it cost?
- How much time will it take?

- How will quality be ensured?

- How will the project team continue to exceed the customer's expectations?

- What will be the effects on other project activities?

- How will the project manager involve and communicate with all stakeholders?

Generally, if the change is customer-driven, then funding for the change should be provided by the customer in the form of budget modifications, a contract change order, or an adjustment to the scope. Externally driven mandatory changes–for example, those beyond the control of the project team–should be paid for by the customer. In all cases, the funding for the change should cover all of the costs and must be recorded.

Other types of change will depend on the project situation, but all must be acknowledged through adjustment in budget, schedule, or scope. If the customer will not acknowledge the change and there is no contingency for it, the change may be offset by deleting a lower priority element of scope. The project manager must get the customer's agreement before deleting any element of scope.

It is important to settle the costs of change promptly and fairly.

It is important to determine who will assume responsibility for the cost of the change before the work is undertaken. If there is a question regarding responsibility for the change, both parties must be fair and reasonable. In this situation, a healthy customer relationship is essential to successful change management. Change issues should be settled promptly but should remain open until the information needed to settle them fairly has been obtained.

4. Communicate the Strategy and Gain Endorsement for the Change

The change management plan should include a process for communicating changes to the customer, the enterprise's management, and other key parties. Changes that do not affect the scope may not require the approval of the customer, depending on the project contract. As a general rule of thumb, if the change affects the scope, schedule, budget, deliverables, or the customer's expectations for the final product, the customer should be involved in the disposition of the change.

All changes that are endorsed by the customer will require action: budgets must be adjusted, communication must take place, and care must be taken to ensure that elements that are deleted from the scope do not find their way back into the project. Once the change has been addressed, endorsement by the stakeholders must again take place. For the stakeholders to maintain their commitment to the project, they must be kept fully informed of changes to the project workplan.

5. Revise the Workplan and Monitor the Effects of Change

Once the planned response has been communicated and endorsed, it can be implemented. During implementation, two additional tasks should be performed. First, the project manager needs to ensure that the workplan is adjusted to account for the change. Although the effect of the change upon workplan elements may already have been assessed and endorsed, the actual revisions must now be documented in the workplan.

Monitor the effects of the change.

Second, the project manager should install a means to monitor the effects of change. Depending on the magnitude of the change, the monitoring may be either incorporated into the next standard project review or conducted more frequently.

Managing Change Internally

Even with an effective change management plan in place, it will not be possible to eliminate all changes. However, the project manager can do much internally to prevent and control changes related to scope creep, increased level of effort, quality creep, new technologies and tools, and personnel, which are defined in Types and Sources of Change, page 170.

Scope Creep

Frequently, the customer initiates a change that results in scope creep, rarely with any intent to create a significant change. Often, the initial effect on cost and schedule appears to be small. If the customer's objectives are weakly defined, then the scope creep is difficult to detect initially and can increase cost, delay the schedule, or affect the work breakdown structure.

Scope creep can be generated by the project team as well. Frequently, we recognize it in the form of minor adjustments to the deliverables that are intended to be in the customer's best interests even if they add some cost or create a functional change that the customer did not request. Scope creep may originate with team members' discussions with the customer's representatives or in small work groups within the team, so the project manager may not be aware of scope creep until a project report shows a task to be over budget or behind schedule.

A well-defined scope can minimize scope creep.

Scope creep can be minimized by having a well-defined scope that is supported by the work breakdown structure. The project manager can begin to control scope creep by using the change management plan to provide guidance to the task managers and the team members so they can adequately manage scope creep. Endorsement of the project workplan will validate the criteria with which to measure scope creep.

Level of Effort

If the project manager does not manage change, scope creep can lead to increases in level of effort. Increases in level of effort invariably translate into increased costs and delayed schedules and often cause other types of changes to occur in a continuing snowball effect.

In developing budgets and schedules that reflect a level of effort for project scope, project managers and team members rely on experience with similar projects. However, team members may disagree on the level of effort based on their understanding of the complexities of the new project. If this lack of agreement is not acknowledged and addressed at the beginning of the project, it can lead to unmanaged increases in level of effort.

Certain activities commonly result in an increased level of effort and should be red flags for a project manager during the planning and execution phases of a project. These activities include the continual refinement of alternatives and concepts beyond those defined in the scope and the application of a higher level of technology than the customer expects or is willing to fund, under the reasoning that it is in the customer's best interest. These activities when left unmanaged rarely produce results of value and are usually harmful to the project.

The project manager can control the level of effort by careful development of the change management plan during the planning phase, by complete endorsement of the project, and by frequent communication with the project team and the customer on the status of the project in relation to the workplan.

Quality Creep

Quality creep is the subtle change that occurs when an individual deviates from the quality standards developed for the project. Generally, quality creep occurs as individuals apply their own definition of quality, which often differs from what is specified in the workplan.

> **A**nticipate the potential for quality creep during the selection of team members.

The project manager can anticipate the potential for quality creep during the selection of team members. Team members who do not have experience delivering projects at the quality specified for this project should be carefully coached.

Quality creep can be best controlled by developing the quality standards for the project, based on the customer's needs and expectations, early in the project planning phase. Metrics with which to measure the application of the quality standards will help ensure a mutual understanding and help minimize quality creep. This understanding should be documented in a quality management plan, a component of the project workplan (see the monograph *Plan Project*). Gaining a mutual understanding requires that the project manager continually emphasize and clarify the alignment between the customer's vision and expectations and the scope. Quality creep can be detected early if team members who clearly understand the customer's expectations are alert to the problem as they review work completed.

Technologies and Tools

Most enterprises are committed to the development of new, customer-focused technologies and tools and their cost-effective application to the customer's projects. However, the unfocused application of new technologies and tools can lead to unfulfilled customer expectations and to project cost and schedule problems. Problems associated with inappropriately using new technologies and tools are often part of scope creep, inappropriate level of effort, or quality creep. Recognition of the problem can occur as part of the quality management process of the project, for example, by comparing the application of the new technologies and tools with their intended use as described in the scope and with the customer's needs and expectations.

The project manager should describe the intended use of any new technologies and tools during the development of the project workplan. This intended use should have the endorsement of both the customer and those responsible for the correct application of the technology or tool. If the customer representatives have not endorsed the use, then they will be surprised, which can adversely affect the customer-enterprise relationship.

The project manager can control the changes to the project caused by inappropriate use of new technologies and tools by understanding where they add value, how they help meet customer expectations, and how they will be applied. Team members must be thoroughly coached and instructed on the appropriate use of new technologies and tools. When new technologies and tools are first introduced to projects, only a limited number of people are available who understand the correct application. These people must be incorporated into the project during times of technology or tool application and project review.

Personnel Changes

High-performance teams are a result of selecting the best people for the project, chartering the team, building the team, and going through the endorsement process. After this process is completed, high performance is achieved by maintaining the continuity of the team so that the work that has gone into developing the team can contribute to fulfilling customer expectations. Changing members of the team typically reduces team performance. However, the effect of staffing changes on the performance of the team and the outcome of the project can vary greatly, depending on how the change is managed.

At the beginning of a project, all parties have the best intentions to maintain the continuity of the project team. However, situations in the enterprise and personal matters can affect staffing. During the planning phase, project managers should recognize that some team members may leave during the project and should identify the process for accommodating this change. The process must identify under what conditions staff changes will be considered, since continuity of the team is of utmost importance to maintaining high performance.

If staff changes occur, they should be made in a manner that creates the least amount of disruption and that results in no deterioration of the customer relationship. Remembering that the customer has endorsed the original project workplan, the customer will also need to endorse a staff change if that change will affect the customer's perception of how their expectations will be met.

Responsibilities for Managing Change

The Project Manager

The project manager is responsible for managing change, including the authorization of any changes to the budget and schedule. This responsibility requires the personal involvement of the project manager in the development of the change management plan.

The project manager is the primary contact for the customer and therefore is in the best position for early identification of customer-initiated changes. As the primary contact, the project manager has the opportunity to prepare the customer for team-initiated or externally-initiated change, eliminating the surprise that often accompanies change.

The project manager is also responsible for communicating the importance of change management to the team. The project manager must emphasize and monitor the management of quality, particularly ensuring that the level of quality matches the customer's expectations. The change management plan will provide the guidelines, and the endorsement will provide the commitment and account-ability.

The Team

Team members must control and manage change in their area of responsibility. Typically, team members can exercise the most control over changes created by increases in level of effort and, to a certain extent, scope creep.

Team members can frequently identify potential changes to the project that can have either positive or negative effects. They have a responsibility to the customer to bring forth ideas that add value as well as potential circumstances that could result in negative change.

The Customer

The customer is responsible for understanding the potential for change in a project; reviewing and discussing potential and real changes with the project manager as they are identified; and reaching agreement on a desirable course of action and endorsing that action. The project manager should discuss these responsibilities with the customer during the planning phase.

Summary

Because change is so common to projects, the ability of a project manager to effectively manage change may mean the difference between average and excellent performance during the execution phase of the project delivery process. Unfortunately, change has been viewed as an undesirable aspect of project management, and therefore project managers do not like to confront it. But project managers should anticipate it; plan for it, through the development of a change management plan; and take responsibility for managing it, particularly internal change. Through early identification and analysis of change and through development of a plan, a project manager can efficiently respond to change. If the project manager keeps the customer and project team informed when change occurs, change can be endorsed as part of the workplan. By monitoring change once a response strategy has been implemented, a project manager can ensure that change is controlled.

Other Resources

Bachner, John Philip. 1991. *Practice Management for Design Professionals: A Practical Guide to Avoiding Liability and Enhancing Profitability.* New York: John Wiley & Sons, Inc.

Bridges, William. 1991. *Managing Transitions: Making the Most of Change.* Reading, MA: Addison-Wesley.

Fisher, Roger, and William Ury. 1984. *Getting to Yes: Negotiating Agreement Without Giving In.* Baltimore, MA: Penguin.

Close Project

OVERVIEW

Close Project is the final monograph in this series because once all closure activities have been completed, the project delivery process has reached an end.

Despite common misconceptions, project closure should begin during the planning phase of a project when the workplan is developed, not in the final stages of a project. Closure activities should be ongoing activities throughout the life of a project. In this way, project closure can be completed in an efficient and timely manner as part of budgeted activities and not as a poorly executed afterthought that is a burden on a project budget.

This monograph covers the development of the closure plan at the beginning of the project and the activities that should occur during project execution and final closeout.

Introduction

Project closure as a defined project delivery activity is frequently overlooked, yet it is an essential activity in successful project delivery. The project manager who recognizes project closure as a strategic part of the project delivery process will have greater success managing the outcome of the project and meeting the expectations of the stakeholders.

Project closure provides a unique opportunity for the project manager to capture and distribute the experience, skills, and knowledge that have been developed during a project. This intellectual capital must be leveraged for its business development, technical, and project delivery values. So, even though a project is complete, it can still contribute to the strategic objectives of the enterprise.

Historically, project closure has been viewed as a series of activities that occurred at the end of the project and was generally clerical in nature. However, project closure should be thought of as an ongoing process whose activities begin in the planning phase and continue through final closure and archiving. The activities associated with project closure can be divided into three chronological stages:

- Beginning of the project — Planning for closure

- During the project — Ongoing closure activities

- End of the project — Final closure activities

After discussing the benefits of an ongoing, thorough process for project closure, activities associated with closure are discussed in terms of these three stages.

Benefits of Closure

If project closure is not adequately planned for or is simply left as an unpleasant task at the end of the project, this activity will be expensive and incomplete, project performance will suffer, and the potential for additional projects with the customer will be jeopardized. However, well-planned project closure provides great benefits to all of the project stakeholders including the customer, the enterprise, the project manager, and the project team members. Understanding these benefits helps eliminate the common perspective that closure is an unpleasant but necessary evil.

Benefits to the Customer

Project closure has value for the customer if it results in a thorough project record with easy-to-retrieve information.

Project closure has value for the customer if it results in a thorough project record with easy-to-retrieve information. Customers are often annoyed if the enterprise is unable to respond to requests for information after the product has been delivered. In contrast, nothing satisfies a customer more than requesting backup calculations on a structural detail 6 months after project closure and receiving it quickly–simply because the project was properly documented, organized, and archived.

Efforts should always be focused on helping customer representatives be as successful as possible in their own organizations. This success can be communicated by having good access to project records, which can help customer representatives be more responsive to their superiors. Also, success can be communicated through joint activities such as publication of professional papers, presentations to outside organizations, and workshops for interested individuals.

Benefits to the Enterprise

Project closure clearly has value for the enterprise. One of the greatest benefits occurs when lessons learned on projects are incorporated into ongoing technology development and the project delivery process. However, this benefit can only happen when closure is planned at the beginning of the project and implemented throughout the project. Properly planned closure activities allow lessons learned to be transferred in both meaningful and well-understood ways.

The enterprise also benefits from a well-orchestrated closure plan by being able to close the project financially and receive final payment on a timely basis. Lack of closure can lead to unresolved payments that can drag on for months. Often, this is a result of not planning closure activities or not communicating the plan to the project team members.

Benefits to the Team

The project manager has a large stake in a successful project closure plan. The project archives are the last will and testament of the project. Unless the archival process is done well, inquiries about the project will be difficult to respond to, will take excessive project manager time, and may force the project manager to rely solely on memory, a practice that should be avoided.

A hurried and incomplete closure process at the end of the project when the remaining budget is small will be avoided if closure activities occur throughout the project.

Developing a closure plan as part of the project workplan and then closing out tasks as they are completed allow for an orderly and timely exit of team members from the project. When project closure occurs throughout the project, the project manager has an opportunity to review the project archival materials. The project manager will have a sense of accomplishment in the progress of the job and will avoid a hurried and incomplete closure process at the end of the project when the remaining budget is small.

A good closure plan paves the way for the project team members' feelings of personal accomplishment. Items such as deliverables, project references, project résumés, project evaluations provided by the customer, project write-ups, press releases, and publications all help provide a tangible sense of completion of the project and a sense of personal satisfaction and recognition. In order for this to occur effectively, closeout activities that emphasize personal accomplishment must be defined at the beginning of the project.

The Beginning of the Project — Planning for Closure

So that the customer, the enterprise, and the team members receive the full benefit of project closure, planning for closure starts at the beginning of the project during project workplan development. Planning for closure should result in written instructions known as the closure plan, which is a component of the project workplan.

As part of the closure plan, the project manager must consider the procedures for closing the financial elements of the project. Although this is just one of the many elements to consider, the financial success of the project is improved by anticipating and meeting the specific financial requirements of the customer and subcontractors.

The Closure Plan

The project manager should not plan on using the contingency budget to support closure activities.

In preparing the project closure plan, the project manager must accomplish several goals. First and most important, the project must have well-defined tasks in the work breakdown structure and an adequate budget for closure activities. The project manager should not plan on using the contingency budget to support closure activities. Much of the closure process should occur during the project as tasks are completed and will most likely be part of other ongoing activities including:

- Project reviews

- Coordination with the customer

- Periodic removal or purging of temporary items from the files

- Records management

- Demobilization

The project manager must budget for project archiving, project closure meetings, and any follow-up activities that will support the development of promotional material for the enterprise or for the customer.

The project manager should communicate to the team members their roles and responsibilities in project closure. All members of the team, particularly lead personnel responsible for specific tasks, should be aware of what is expected of them for project closure during and at the end of the project. Although there is no prescribed format for a closure plan, the guidance for its development can come from several sources:

- Discussions with the customer

- Requirements of the enterprise

- Requirements of the contract

Discussions with the customer at initial project meetings or workshops, where customers define their needs and expectations, can provide information and insight into activities that will need to be completed as part of project closure. These activities frequently are in the areas of technical backup material and financial material needed for the customer's files. Not only is the type of information important, but the format the customer requires is also important. Customer format needs should determine how these administrative functions are set up.

The enterprise will also have closure requirements, including the need for financial, technical, staffing, and marketing information. For example, the enterprise must complete final billing and receive retainage, and staff evaluations must be complete before the project can be closed. Knowing the particular requirements of the enterprise early in the project makes closure easier.

Finally, the contract identifies requirements that need attention during closure. These requirements, which may be financial, legal, or statutory, must also become part of the project closure plan and be communicated to the project team.

Although the specifics of the closure plan will vary depending on the requirements of the customer, the enterprise, and the contract, most closure plans will contain procedures for the following activities:

- Phasing closure based on tasks in the work breakdown structure

- Demobilizing staff and resources

- Recommending staff development opportunities

- Closing the technical elements of the project

- Conducting a project closure meeting with the customer and reconciling the customer's vision with the final product and service

- Closing the financial elements of the project

- Evaluating, rewarding, and recognizing project team members

- Archiving project material

- Supplying information to the enterprise's business development database

Successful project managers will plan for these closure activities, which occur during and at the end of the project, so that the schedule can be met. Extending the schedule is expensive, and early identification of these activities in a closure plan will help ensure that they are accomplished in a timely manner.

Financial Closure Preparation

The success of closure is heavily vested in a carefully planned financial project setup.

Financial success of projects is important to the well-being of both the enterprise and the customer and needs special comment at this point. The success of closure is heavily vested in a carefully planned financial project setup. The ability to do timely audits at the end of the project and be compensated for all earned value and any retainage is linked to the ability to track costs throughout the life of the project.

When setting up the financial control systems at the beginning of a project, consider the end result and how the project will be closed contractually and administratively from a financial perspective. Also, consider the customer: priority should be given to accommodating their needs and expectations. For example, if the customer wants to account for expenses, a detailed invoice itemizing expenses should be developed, and receipts and backup information for expenses should be saved and made readily available. There is nothing more frustrating to a project manager than to find at the end of the project that the reimbursable expenses are disallowed simply because the right information to support the expenses was not kept. Giving consideration to financial closure of the project at the beginning of the project will help avoid these unexpected costs.

Specific attention should be given to the documentation required of subcontractors. Many of them are small businesses that may not possess systems and procedures to properly document costs incurred. Early discussions with subcontractors of the cost documentation requirements of both the enterprise and the customer will prevent payment problems later on.

During the Project — Ongoing Closure

To overcome the misconception that project closure occurs at the end of the project, it is worthwhile to look at the types of closure activities that can and should occur during the project. Some of the more significant closure activities include:

- Phased closure of tasks
- Demobilization
- Staff development
- Technical closure

Phased Closure of Tasks

As previously mentioned, tasks are the main components of the work breakdown structure. By definition, a task has defined beginning and end points. Using a well-defined work breakdown structure, the project manager can successfully prepare for final project closure by closing the project incrementally: closing individual tasks as they are completed. If the project does not have a good work breakdown structure, project closure will be difficult. (For information on work breakdown structures, see the monograph *Plan Project.*)

As individual tasks are completed and closed, the associated project billing numbers are closed. Therefore, project costs can be efficiently tracked and overall expenditure of project resources can be controlled. The project manager must remember that, even though individual tasks are closed, charges incurred by other tasks will show up somewhere in the project budget. Therefore, the project manager must identify in the closure plan how the project numbers will be handled, how and when they will be closed, and who will be responsible for them. Generally, project numbers should be set up for tracking closure costs, allowing other tasks to be closed in a timely way. The project manager can then focus on the remaining efforts to close the project–the closure meeting, archiving of materials, and communicating the project success–without jeopardizing the payments associated with the principal project deliverables.

The project work breakdown structure should clearly indicate to the team what constitutes completion of each task. And the closure plan should reinforce this and guide the team through orderly task closure. A well-conceived closure plan keeps the appropriate staff working on each task until the task is complete, then

The project manager can successfully prepare for final project closure by closing the project incrementally.

an organized and orderly process to demobilize staff is implemented (see the following section). This process allows better use of resources as they become available and as tasks are completed and the project winds down.

Demobilization

The closure plan should include a strategy for demobilizing staff, including professional, technical, clerical, and out-sourced staff. The project manager must be careful not to demobilize the staff too early. Remobilizing staff in order to complete an unanticipated requirement for the customer could jeopardize the performance of a project. On the other hand, should the project drag on, it would be easy to overrun the budget by not having staff demobilized in a timely fashion.

The most critical element to project team demobilization is having a well-conceived staffing plan tied to a schedule that reflects key deliverables and milestones.

For large-scale projects (multi-month or multi-year with fees exceeding $500,000), the project manager may find that demobilizing the project team can be as difficult, if not more difficult, as mobilizing the team. The key to effective and timely project team demobilization is having a well-conceived staffing plan tied to a schedule that reflects key deliverables and milestones. When the project or individual major tasks approach 50 to 75 percent completion, the demobilization strategies should be reviewed in increasing detail and implemented in a timely way.

Consideration should also be given to defining a core group of team members that will stay intact through project closure. This core group is the key contact for the customer on matters related to the project prior to the archiving of the material and final project closure. The project manager should have a plan that identifies the minimum number of people necessary to respond to potential project issues or claims.

Project managers may find it difficult to determine when enough is enough with respect to completing a scope of work — particularly a scope of work that is difficult to define, such as a study, regulatory support, or other consulting work not tied to specific products, such as design plan sheets. Therefore, demobilization strategies should be highly visible to both the team and to the customer and tied to a detailed project schedule and milestones. Then certain resources will be removed as parts of the project are completed, submitted, approved, and accepted by the customer.

In addition to demobilizing staff resources, the project manager should look at the demobilization and redeployment of nonstaff resources, such as equipment, software, vehicles, and, on large projects, a dedicated project office. The phaseout of these resources should be well planned before the last 10 percent of the project when team members are absorbed in getting the product to the customer. Early planning will help avoid frustration and excessive nonreimbursable expenses.

Staff Development

The project manager should also include in the project closure plan procedures for making staff development recommendations. These recommendations should be circulated to individuals in the enterprise responsible for staff development. The staff development recommendations could include training that would further develop core skills and experience gained during the project. Also, opportunities for new project assignments that would help improve and expand on the experience and core skills of an individual should be carefully considered throughout the course of the project and be included as part of the closure activities for staff development. Staff involvement in other related assignments provides a direct benefit to the enterprise by increasing the technical knowledge and skill base of project team members.

Technical Closure

Technical closure is the review and acknowledgment that appropriate technology has been used and that the customer has benefited from that technology. Technical closure is also the acknowledgment that the enterprise has benefited from the use of the technologies through technology transfer to other people and projects in the enterprise. Although this would seem to apply to the use of new and innovative technologies, there is a need to acknowledge and communicate that our well-established technologies have also been used appropriately and effectively.

The knowledge of effective use of new or existing technology can provide tremendous value to the enterprise, since the approach used originally can be repeated with less effort on similar projects. By summarizing the results of effective technology application and distributing it to other staff that have responsibility for development and implementation of that technology, the knowledge gained by the project team can be used by all stakeholders.

Technological information should be leveraged throughout the enterprise in an on-going process.

Technical closure should begin during the review of products as tasks are completed and should continue until the end of the project. Technical closure is best done as the project progresses so that lessons learned can be applied to later stages of the project and can be applied to other projects as early as possible.

The project team should review the project to see if the appropriate resources and technologies were used in the best interests of the customer and in the most efficient, cost-effective manner. If new technologies were used, discuss the strengths and weaknesses of these technologies and how they might be used in the future. If new methods of using an existing technology have particularly positive or negative results, these should be noted as well.

In addition to leveraging technologies on other projects, technological experience can be leveraged through proposals and other business development and marketing materials. Intellectual capital relative to technology is valuable for a limited time — about 3 to 4 years. Therefore, it is critical for the enterprise to gather and distribute this information in a timely manner so that the enterprise can effectively apply core skills and innovations to gain a competitive advantage.

The project team should also consider writing articles or papers for trade publications or professional organizations whose membership would be interested in the technology. The public relations for the enterprise and for the customer is good, and the enterprise's relationship with the customer can be enhanced by jointly producing and presenting these materials.

Whether the technological experience is used for enhancing project performance or for marketing activities, the project manager should identify the appropriate pathways for information distribution. Asking the following questions can help identify the right resources:

- What information about the technology used on this project would be of interest to other projects and other customers?

- How can this information be transferred most effectively?

End of the Project — Closing the Project

Project closure at the end of the project marks the end of all project administration. All tasks must be closed, all financial details must be completed, and the complete project record must be archived.

Project closure marks the fulfillment of all customer needs and expectations. The project manager must provide the customer all deliverables, including a complete project record, and must offer a final opportunity to provide feedback on the enterprise's performance.

This section discusses project closure activities, including:

- Project closure meeting
- Financial closure
- Project evaluation, reward, and recognition
- Archiving
- Business development

Although all of these activities are planned for at the beginning of the project, most of the work associated with these activities occurs at the end of the project.

Project Closure Meeting

Final project closure activities can be triggered by a project closure meeting. In this way, a defined endpoint for the project exists. This meeting, or series of meetings, should have a formal agenda and should involve the customer and other stakeholders to help arrive at complete closure on all the important project issues. The project manager should then draft a letter to the customer summarizing the events of the project meeting and acknowledging that all the deliverables, products, and requirements have been met.

The project closure meeting can also be structured to communicate the success of the project to the customer's senior management. This communication could be done by organizing the closure meeting in three parts. Part 1 would be internal to the enterprise and the project team. Part 2 would include the project team's customer counterpart(s) to discuss the closure requirements and resolve any discrepancies. Part 3 would involve the customer's senior management, who would confirm the completion of the project and set the stage for formal project closure.

During the project team's closure meeting, the initial vision should be compared with the final project results to ensure that all objectives have been met. If there are significant changes between the initial vision and the final results, a discussion should be held to determine how those changes occurred and how well they were managed. A review should also be conducted regarding how the project team identified customer expectations and what methods the team would recommend other project teams use. This discussion helps the project team gain greater clarity about the degree of project success, including the extent to which the project met the customer's needs and expectations. This discussion may also enable the project manager to communicate the project's success to the customer.

The closure meeting provides an excellent opportunity to discuss follow-up work.

Regardless of whether project closure involves the customer's senior management or project team members only, the goal of the meeting is to identify any expectations that have not been met and to propose solutions that would allow the project to be closed out financially, technically, and contractually to the full satisfaction of all parties. The closure meeting also provides an excellent opportunity to discuss potential follow-up work. (See Business Development, page 209.)

Financial Closure

Typical financial closure activities that occur at the end of a project include submitting the final bill, obtaining any retainage associated with the project, and closing out any subconsultant contracts. In addition, financial performance should be measured and compared to planned objectives.

Submitting the Final Bill

A critical part of the project accounting process is a review of any remaining costs that have not already been recognized as income or billed to the customer. A critical review of the contract requirements and project accounting records should be undertaken to ensure the appropriateness and completeness of all charges that should have been billed to the customer at this point. Timely processing of all expense items, such as subcontractor invoices and expense reports, is imperative. Following this critical review, the enterprise is able to send the customer a truly final bill.

Retainage

Many projects have retainage associated with them, which represents earnings withheld pending outcome of an identifiable aspect of the project (for example, project completion or project auditing). The sooner the project can be closed out, the sooner the enterprise receives the outstanding retainage from the customer. It is not uncommon for retainage to be held by a customer for several years. While this money is being held by the customer on the enterprise's behalf, opportunities associated with the investment of those funds are lost. One strategy for minimizing this problem is to link retainage to tasks. By linking retainage with individual tasks, reimbursement can be received incrementally as tasks are completed.

Subconsultant Contract Closure

Close out subconsultant activities in a timely and expedient manner.

Too often the project manager overlooks the effect of subconsultant contracts on the financial closure of projects. The project manager should have a process in place that allows the closure of subconsultant activities in a timely and expedient manner. Also, this process should be communicated to the subconsultant along with information on contract billing, audits, and other requirements necessary to close out the contract.

Financial Performance

Financial closure also requires the project manager to develop financial measures during the workplanning that will help compare a project's financial performance to the financial elements of the workplan. The closure plan developed during the project planning phase must contain the necessary cost information and performance criteria to contribute to the financial database of the enterprise so that the costs of delivering projects can be evaluated. Part of this effort should involve coordination with the appropriate business group so that the information generated during the financial performance review can be evaluated and used for future scoping, pricing, and pursuit of similar projects.

The financial lessons learned should address issues such as project setup, billings, how cash flow or burn rate was accomplished, conformance to the customer's budget requirements, and overall financial performance of the enterprise. The project manager should work with his or her business group to set up the appropriate criteria in the project closure plan to be monitored and measured. The focus is not only on financial performance but also on developing a record to help estimate pricing and scoping of future projects that are similar in nature or for which the customer uses similar pricing and scoping procedures.

Project Evaluation, Reward, and Recognition

At the end of the project, an evaluation of staff, including project management, provides a metric of performance. Reward and recognition for those who have significantly contributed to the success of the project also provide acknowledgment of individuals and of the project.

Staff Evaluation

As part of the early planning activities, the project manager is responsible for staff development associated with the professional resources the enterprise puts under his or her authority. At the end of the project, the project manager has a responsibility to the enterprise and a professional obligation to the staff assigned to the project to provide individual and team evaluations. Therefore, the project manager should include procedures in the closure plan for exit evaluations. These procedures should address how the evaluations will be conducted, documented, and distributed to the appropriate people.

Project Management Evaluation

In addition to staff evaluations, project management should be evaluated. The project management performance evaluation provides the means to document project priorities and special considerations at the beginning of the project, serves as a guide during project execution, and then measures performance over the life of the project. The project manager initiates the process during the project setup and then initiates the evaluation activities either during project closure or whenever his or her assignment is complete. During closure, the project manager and a senior representative of the enterprise should review the project and review the results of the project manager evaluation. Other primary stakeholders can be involved in the evaluation, if appropriate.

Reward and Recognition

One of the items often overlooked in project closure is the reward and recognition of those who have contributed to the success of the project. At the beginning of a project, the project manager should anticipate the kinds of reward and recognition most appropriate for the project; for example, individual recognition or opportunities to co-author a paper with a customer. This technical recognition can often be budgeted for and included as part of the project contingency, provided the customer is willing and the project is successful. As the project end nears, the project manager should look for mutually beneficial opportunities for reward and recognition using project funds. The emphasis of reward and recognition should be on communicating personal, technical, and service successes internally and externally; communicating customer successes wherever possible; and leveraging relationships with the customer by communicating the project's success.

Archiving

The archiving method should be tailored to the size and complexity of the project.

Although the project archive is incomplete until the end of the project, the project manager should plan for archiving at the beginning of the project and should perform some archiving tasks throughout the project. Like the financial management system, the archiving method should be tailored to the size and complexity of the project and comply with legal and contractual requirements.

The project manager should set a deadline for archive completion and develop a budget for the archiving process. Many customers allow charges for archiving as billable time, since project closure and records management is of benefit to the customer, particularly in terms of future litigation and claims management.

Project closure is the responsibility of the project manager, but archiving is a task that, if well planned, can be delegated to a project assistant. The project manager should not simply ask the project assistant to do the archiving but should provide specific direction regarding what to archive, when to archive, and how to organize information.

At the beginning of the project, the project manager should develop guidelines for archiving and communicate those guidelines to the project team through the closure plan. Careful planning should be done at the beginning of the project and agreements with the customer made in terms of what the project archives will include, what the archiving process will be, what will be turned over to the customer during project closure, what the format will be, and whether customer archival materials will be originals or copies.

Remove incomplete work or abandoned work from the project files.

If archiving occurs throughout the project, then, at the end of the project, the project manager will not be faced with a major effort of removing nonessential information from the project files. It is particularly important to remove incomplete work or abandoned work so that this material will not be used mistakenly by others.

Items that should be considered for archiving include the project records and communications, backup studies, databases used to derive the design drawings or design conclusions, computer files, and spreadsheets. Archival materials for the customer should be identified in the closure plan, covered in the budget, and made available during project closure in a format acceptable to the customer.

Business Development

In order to ensure the continued success of the enterprise, the project manager must understand the relationship that project closure has with the enterprise's ongoing procurement process. Once the project manager understands this relationship, he or she will realize that although project closure marks the end of the current project, it marks the beginning of securing additional projects for the enterprise.

Obviously, project closure provides an excellent opportunity to identify potential follow-up work to the existing job. The project manager should look for aspects of the overall project that could be pursued beyond the project closure. If that follow-up work is related to the existing work, then new work could be agreed to in the form of a supplement, a new contract, or another mechanism that the customer might find expedient in moving the follow-up work ahead. An extension of a project is typically easier for a customer to sell to management or funding agencies than new work. On the other hand, if the customer asks the enterprise to do work that is not related to the existing project and would be considered out of scope, this work should be performed under a separate contract. Regardless of the kind of contractual agreement to be made, the project manager should meet with the customer representatives to ensure that the closure activities for the current project are completed with respect to the original scope of work. This creates a clean slate for additional work.

In addition to follow-up work with the existing customer, project closure includes activities that help position the enterprise for new work with existing and potential customers. Formally, this occurs through a database of business development information. Informally, gained knowledge from the execution of the project can be applied to current and future customers.

The shelf life of most project descriptions is 5 years at most, so it is important to replenish the database with fresh project descriptions that can highlight core skills innovatively and competitively. An up-to-date database lets the enterprise leverage any leading-edge and emerging technologies associated with the project in a way that increases the enterprise's competitive strength in the marketplace. Because of the time-sensitive nature of business development materials, project managers must ensure that the database is updated throughout the project and on a regular basis.

The project manager is obligated to develop project-related information that can help support the enterprise's business development objectives.

Having been entrusted with the enterprise's resources, the project manager is obligated to develop project-related information that can help support the enterprise's business development objectives and, therefore, the enterprise's continued success.

Summary

Project closure is an ongoing activity that begins with developing a closure plan during the planning phase of the project, continues during the execution of the project as tasks are closed out incrementally and staff is demobilized, and ends when all closure requirements have been met. These requirements include meeting the needs and expectations of the customer, archiving the project records, and submitting a final bill.

Often, project closure is an overlooked element of the project delivery process that is quickly and incompletely executed at the end of the project when there is little time and budget. However, when project managers plan for closure, the customer, the enterprise, and the project team benefit. The customer has a thorough project record with easy-to-retrieve information. The enterprise can leverage project team experience on other projects as technical and financial information is disseminated throughout the enterprise. The project manager and other team members can gain a sense of personal accomplishment as completed tasks are closed out and tangible records of individual and team contributions are made.